# Letters from Eleanor Roosevelt

A Novel

To request permissions, contact the publisher at business@parkroadpublishing.com

Paperback: 978-1-7375778-8-1
Ebook: 978-1-7375778-9-8



FIRST EDITION JUNE 2022

Edited by Hunter Bishop
Cover art by Mary Swigonski & Hunter Bishop Layout by Hunter Bishop

Drink deeply and enjoy this space between reality and dream, a space where tomorrows are planted, nurtured, and grow. Here's to tomorrows' tomorrow, may it be a place where human dignity is nurtured and sustained in small things, in small places close to home.

The future belongs to those who believe in the beauty of dreams.

Eleanor Roosevelt.

To Eleanor Roosevelt for her embodiment of the power that is love.

To MaryLou Ramsey for her patience and abiding love.

## *Main Characters*

Joan Zatańczy—Born in Roosevelt, New Jersey. She is finishing her junior year at Barnard College. The daughter of Eva and Bronislaw Zatańczy.

Eva Zatańczy—wife of Bronislaw, mother of Joan. Pen pal with Eleanor Roosevelt.

Bronislaw Zatańczy (Brony)—Eva's husband, father of Joan, Anastasia's brother.

Anastasia Zatańczy (Stasia)—Bronislaw's sister, Eva's sister-in-law, a nurse first in New York City, then near Roosevelt, New Jersey.

Eleanor Roosevelt—the longest serving First Lady of the United States, from 1933 until 1945. Wife of Franklin Roosevelt, 32nd President of the United States. United States delegate to the United Nations General Assembly from 1945 until 1952.

Yanina Folkman Kominiarski—Joan's best friend and neighbor in Roosevelt, New Jersey, where they both grew up. Yanina graduated from high school and moved to *Kasefet Kibbutz* in Israel, where she now lives with her husband, Simcha.

Golda Stein—sister to Yanina and Avraham's maternal grandmother. After the war years, she and her husband, Janusz, raised Yanina and Avraham. Joan, Yanina and Avraham call her *Bubba* (Yiddish for grandmother).

Janusz Stein—Golda Stein's husband. Joan, Yanina and Avraham call him *Zayde* (Yiddish for grandfather).

The Stein's and the Zatańczy's are neighbors in a duplex home in Roosevelt, NJ.

# Letters From Eleanor Roosevelt

# *Part I*
# *Summer 1961*

Joan Zatańczy at Barnard College, New York City, USA to Yanina Kominiarski at Kasefet Kibbutz, Israel

June 7, 1961

Dear Yanina,

Today I am 21! My life is nearly perfect. So why am I waiting for the other shoe to drop? I'm a senior at Barnard with only one more year until I graduate and become an alumna. My advisor has become a dear friend, and I think I'm falling in love! I love my life. What could possibly go wrong?

My birthday celebration has my head spinning. Mama gave me a present that has me gob smack flabbergasted. And Dr. Smyth promised me a picnic when he gets back from his trip to Stanford. I'm counting the days until he gets back.

Mama and Aunt Stasia came to Barnard to celebrate with me. On their way from New Jersey to New York and to my apartment, they stopped at Zabar's on Broadway at 80$^{th}$. Zabar's is so much more than a grocery story. I love their coffee and tea, bagels and bread, every bakery sweet you can imagine, deli meats and cheeses. They have all of that and more.

Mama says Zabar's is worth the extra stop to smell the sugar and chocolate in the bakery (Mama loves her sugar, I inherited that from her). She loves to sample the cheeses in the deli. You should hear Mama go on about "How are they able to give away so many samples and still stay in business?" Aunt Stasia has to say, "Because they charge those prices." You should hear Aunt Stasia go on about Zabar's salad bar.

It was Mama and Aunt Stasia's first visit to my new apartment, and I really wanted them to like it. I tried to be calm, but my nerves kept me pacing in circles while I waited for them to get here. I opened the door for them and Mama scanned the apartment and kept looking, like she expected to see more. Aunt Stasia stuck her head in the door and said it was cozy.

I lost count of how many trips it took from the car to haul up all the bags. They covered my table and the floor with grocery bags and presents. That table is my dining room and office. Mama walked along the wall with my kitchen cabinets, stove, sink, and refrigerator and started opening cabinet doors while Aunt Stasia handed her groceries from the bags. The two of them together are an unstoppable force, so I collapsed on the sofa Dr. Smyth and I found at the Goodwill Store and watched them take over my kitchen space as they set out our dinner.

Dinner started at sunset with the three of us around the table, the classic Zatańczy birthday eve dinner. I never even thought anything about starting to celebrate things at sunset the night before an event until I got to Barnard. In Roosevelt it wasn't a Jewish thing, it was just what everyone just did. But, in Roosevelt everyone is Jewish, except Mama, Aunt Stasia and me.

Mama and Aunt Stasia outdid themselves at Zabar's salad bar, which has every vegetable and salad known to god and man, some not even known to god. Aunt Stasia was adamant—my twenty-first birthday eve dinner had to start with her special wedge salad—crisp iceberg lettuce, diced tomatoes, zucchini, bacon crumbles, raisins, walnuts, all slathered with luscious, creamy blue cheese dressing. And yes, as Aunt Stasia was putting the salad together, she said it! "On birthdays and holidays the raisins and nuts reign. It isn't a celebration if there are no nuts."

Last night, Aunt Stasia said one of her favorite nuts was missing.

We all miss you, Yanina. I miss how we lived side by side, next door to each other in Roosevelt. After you and Avraham escaped from Poland after the war, you always knew you would make your Aliyah to Israel, to build a world safe for all Jews. How is it possible that you have been in Israel working in Kasefet kibbutz for five years?

You could always see your dream. I just dreamt of a world beyond our Roosevelt. Roosevelt is perfect for Mama and Aunt Stasia—two sisters-in-law, living together, grieving the husband and brother they lost in the war. They each seem content enough. But I want more than content. I want more than a quiet life in Roosevelt, New Jersey, where everyone knows everybody and everybody's business.

Then I read that newspaper article about Dean Millicent McIntosh accepting the title of President of Barnard College and a light went on for me. Barnard College was a place where women found their place in the world. I was in eighth grade, and I found my path out of Roosevelt, I would go to Barnard College.

At supper last night, Aunt Stasia being Aunt Stasia, she handed me my salad saying wedgies are one of her favorite things to give on birthdays. That broke Mama and Aunt Stasia up. They still love to laugh at a double entendre. Sometimes I feel like the two of them have their secrets and I'm an outsider. Why? We all live together in the same house. Why do I feel like I'm missing something?

But then Aunt Stasia got serious and said, "Joan, I know you think your Mama and I are salad crazy. But salads feed our bodies and souls. We select, collect and layer the vegetables, cheeses and even meats for the salad; we select, collect and layer friends and experiences in our lives. We chop, slice, and dice to bring our salad together, and we slice and dice our experiences to understand their depths and complexity in our lives. We gather everything into a bowl, adding dressing and placing it on plates to enjoy it; and we gather, dress, and present ourselves to the world. We do all of that to nurture and sustain body and soul, we do that to strengthen family and build community. Too often we eat without thinking. But it is important to be mindful of how we nurture ourselves. Sharing our salads is how we sustain our common union as a family."

Yanina, Aunt Stasia was deep into one of her Buddhist moments. She has a way of making even mundane moments sacred. What Aunt Stasia said, it was a benediction, a blessing. It made the salad a sacrament. Before, I just ate the salad. Now I will remember the layers, the connections and the implications.

After dinner, the night got seriously strange. We finished eating and cleaning up, Aunt Stasia and Mama gave me their regular presents, then Mama put a brown paper grocery bag on the table. I didn't notice it when we were bringing in the bags; but that bag was ancient, with more creases and wrinkles than the face of a 100-year-old lady.
Mama looked wistful and said, "Joan, I'm not at all sure I want to give this to you. But I suppose it's time. Anyway, one letter is for you."

I sat there staring. I wanted to rip into it, but I was afraid to touch that bag. I do not want to know what those stains are! I just hope that one big stain is ketchup.
Aunt Stasia watched me, laughed her Buddha belly laugh and said, "Go on, open it."

I took out the letter sitting on the top—addressed to me, dated right after I was born, and from Mrs. Eleanor Roosevelt. A letter from Mrs. Eleanor Roosevelt to me! THE Mrs. Eleanor Roosevelt!! To me!!!

Mama sighed and talked about how she and Aunt Stasia could see that I was struggling to find a topic for my senior thesis, and they thought those letters might help me, and that is why they gave them to me now.

Yanina, Mama gave me a whole sack of letters from Mrs. Eleanor Roosevelt, starting from back when our little Roosevelt, New Jersey, used to be Jersey Homesteads. (I keep forgetting our town changed its name from Jersey Homesteads to Roosevelt after President Franklin Roosevelt died.) Yanina, how did I not know that Mama and Mrs. Roosevelt are pen pals? How did I not notice who she was writing to every month? Imagine. An entire grocery bag of letters from Eleanor Roosevelt—to Mama.

I asked Mama how she and Mrs. Roosevelt started writing to each other, but you know Mama. She said, "It's a long story" and changed the subject. I have to get Aunt Stasia alone to get that story. Anyway, I stayed up half the night last night reading those letters.

Half way through the bag, I had to check out my collection of quotes, and sure enough, I have eight in there from Mrs. Roosevelt. She said, "You gain strength, courage and confidence by every experience in which you stop to look fear in the face. You are able to say to yourself, I lived through this horror. I can take the next thing that comes along." She also said, "When will our consciences grow so tender that we will act to prevent human misery rather than avenge it?"

I'm sending you a copy of the letter from Mrs. Roosevelt to me. Not that I needed a push, but her letter has me wondering who I am. Just who do I think I am? Sure, I'm a Barnard undergraduate, but I am no different from every Barnard student who wants to graduate and find her place in the world. I know reason and rationality got me into Barnard College. I am 21, an adult, and I have finished three years of college (all of them on the Dean's List with my 4.0 GPA)—I am on my way to graduating and fulfilling my dream— to be a Barnard alum, an educated and empowered woman. But, I am a Zatańczy; I am one who will dance. I keep wondering, what harm can a little fun do? But why do I always feel guilty when I even think of having fun?

Yanina, I wish that you, my first and best friend, could have been here to celebrate with us. I miss our talks. I miss our eavesdropping on our families. Remember how we would hear Aunt Stasia lilting with lightness, Mama sighing as she dragged a dark cloud behind her, Bubba unwavering in righteousness, and Zayde glowing in wisdom and stories. We would listen to them and debate whether life is a delight or a dirge. I miss solving the grand mysteries of the world with you.

But you are 6,000 miles away in Kasefet, Israel, living your dream. Now you are Yanina Kominiarski, married and living on a kibbutz. I miss you so much, but I am glad that you are living your dream. I'm glad that you are happy.

Yours Always,

Joan

Eleanor Roosevelt to Joan Zatańczy

July 25, 1940 (to be delivered in 1961)

Dear Joan,

Welcome to the world. I am writing this welcoming greeting to you shortly after your birth, but at my request to your dear mother, you will not be reading it until you are twenty-one. So, happy twenty-first birthday. I hope it will be a day filled with abiding joy.

I've asked your mother to be discreet with you about our correspondence until you are old enough to understand the importance of circumspection in personal and private matters. You see, as public a person as I am, I am also quite reserved. I prefer to keep my personal relationships personal and private to the extent that this is possible. I do hope you will forgive me for asking your mother to keep a secret from you for all these years.

Joan, at your moment of birth, as you are welcomed into this world, I wonder who you will become.

When my children were young, we played "Who are you?" when we had a visitor with us. One of the children, often Anna, would start. She would choose someone and ask, "Who are you?" If it was Franklin, he would offer his name. Then each of us would take turns asking him, "Who are you?" As he continued to respond, the same answer could not be used twice. After 1933, Franklin would say, President of the United States, then Commander-in-Chief, then perhaps father, brother or son. With each query, the answer became more interesting, deeper, more personal. Each answer required more thoughtfulness and soul searching. The game continued until each person asked everyone else, "Who are you?" Each person had to answer the question at least ten times. We would need to dig deep to find enough qualities to claim as parts of our identity. As we played this game, we got to know each other in interesting ways.

I remember early on I happily said I was mother, wife, sister and helper, as I find great pleasure in being of service to others. As we went around the table, I often wondered who I really am, who I might be becoming.

Today, Joan, I wonder, who are you? Who will you become beyond daughter, friend, niece or student? What experiences will shape your growth, your character? What values will you embody? How will you contribute to our world? I wonder. I hope for you magnificent things, I hope for you love, joy and laughter. I hope for you meaningful contributions that deepen the dignity of your being. Our world is in need of women of strong purpose and gentle hearts. I hope you will be a shining light among women and men.

My dear Joan, at the moment of your birth, and on your twenty-first birthday when you read this, I offer you my very best good wishes. Our church has been a place of solace and comfort for my family. Each year during the New Year's celebration, we sing a lovely blessing song. I am in mind of it now as I gather my wishes for you:

Power of raven be thine
Power of eagle be thine
Power of storm be thine
Power of moon be thine
Power of sea be thine
Power of land be thine
Goodness of sea be thine
Goodness of earth be thine

Joan, I imagine you may find it odd to begin good wishes with the power of ravens, those often maligned black birds. But in old folk lore, ravens are known as tricksters full of humor and wisdom. With good humor and wisdom, I offer my best wishes for you, Joan. I wish for you the powers and strengths of the elements that bring substance to our world. I wish for you joy, love and just enough saltiness to keep your life interesting and tasty.

Fondly,

Mrs. Roosevelt

Joan Zatańczy at Barnard College, New York City, USA to Yanina Kominiarski at Kasefet Kibbutz, Israel

June 10, 1961

Dear Yanina,

I know it is only three days since I wrote to you. But I have so much to tell you, I can't wait another minute. My birthday celebration just keeps getting better! Dr. Smyth—I'm calling him Harold now—got back from his trip to Stanford University, and yesterday he showed up at my apartment with a wicker picnic basket filled with fancy bread, cheese, strawberries, a container of broccoli salad, and a bottle of wine. (He laughed when he said there had to be salad. I like that he remembered, but I'm not sure I like the way he laughed when he said it.). Wine, cheese and salad to celebrate my birthday!

Harold and I walked across the street from the college to the Cathedral of St. John the Divine, to his favorite intimate corner on the Cathedral grounds. He spread out a blanket and we picnicked in the Cathedral's shadow, off by ourselves. We talked and ate and drank wine. We were in our own world. It was bliss. And then he kissed me.

Kissing Harold is poetry. It was better than bliss. We were floating in the ocean. We were body surfing the waves. I could feel the blood surging through me, through every part of me, my whole body was on fire. And that was just the floor play. Then it was the 1812 Overture. You know that part with the horns? You know the cannons are coming, but the horns keep playing, and there are little crescendos, and the strings carry you and carry you, and finally there is the eruption of cannons and chimes and the fireworks light up the sky. Oh, Yanina, for once in my life, I was a free spirit, I was a wild child. I might have been laying under Harold, but my spirit was dancing.

If only there had been more than a thin blanket between me and the rocky ground, it would have been perfect. Still, I come with enough of my own padding to cushion my bones. What a most amazing night! I am an adult at long last. And a woman too. What a night for my first time. And with Harold. It was wonderful.

But, when I got home instead of feeling wonderful, I felt guilty for having fun, especially that kind of fun, in the shadow of the cathedral. I liked being a free spirit, but I don't like always feeling guilty about it.

I love the way Harold and I have become such dear friends in the years since he was my freshman advisor. I love strolling around campus with him, talking endlessly about everything. And now, finally, we are together. He says I am Soigné. I'm his swan.

When I'm with him, I own this place. I feel like I could fly. I am on top of the world. I'm free. I think I could like that feeling if I didn't always get this twitch in the pit of my stomach. Other girls get a hangover after they party. I don't even drink and I get a guilt hangover. I'm haunted by my mother and her superstitions. Mama taught me only too well that wonderful is ephemeral. Freedom and fun never last. I can hear Mama saying it. I can feel myself waiting for the next shoe to drop. But not today. I won't let myself get distracted with worrying about what hasn't happened. Not for my birthday, not this week.

Now I need to focus on finding a topic for my senior thesis. Those letters from Mrs. Roosevelt have to have something I can use! I am going to just keep reading them until I find a topic Smyth will approve.

Yours Always,

Joan

Joan to Yanina

June 20, 1961

Dear Yanina,

Your responses to Mrs. Roosevelt's "Who are you" game have me thinking. You are Yanina, my friend, Avraham's sister, Simcha's wife, and a *kibbutznik*. And you are so much more than that. Yes, you are a daughter to your parents, even if they are dead. And *Bubba* and *Zayde* are both grandparents and parents to you and Avraham. Without a doubt, you are a Zionist and Polish. I hope your dreams of becoming a mother and a teacher come true. You are all of that, and so much more.

When I sat down to answer the question, I quickly discovered the game wasn't so easy. It is hard to put who I am, who I want to be, into words. But here's my try. I am Joan. Disciplined. Determined. Rational. Realistic. Daughter. Niece. Friend. Girl, no woman. And caring. Mama says I care about people to a fault. She says I am incapable of seeing their faults. Maybe she's right, but I want to see the best in people. Aunt Stasia says I see only the best in people; until I don't. What does that even mean?

Yanina, as I read your descriptions of Kasefet, I see echoes of our Roosevelt. Both with 200 families. Both with their Bauhaus buildings—simple, clean, practical. But your Kibbutznicks are even more practical that we are in Roosevelt. I wonder what Roosevelt would have been like if your kibbutz principles of community responsibility, self-reliance, and collective action took hold in the early days. Would Roosevelt's cooperatives still be working? Maybe they could have kept the factory open. But then Mama would not have needed to ask Mrs. Roosevelt for her help, and I wouldn't have this treasure trove of letters from Mrs. Roosevelt.

Your rooms in Kasefet sound bigger than my apartment. We both have a living room and kitchen in one room and a separate bedroom, but you have your our own private bathroom. All the apartments on my floor share the bathroom, which is only two doors down from me. Everyone keeps the bathroom so clean it sparkles. Mrs. Ramirez, next door to me, sets the standard and the rest of us work to keep up. The care and cleaning of our bathroom is a thread that weaves a sense of community on our floor. Everyone does a little more than their share (even Mr. Mola, who none-the-less always leaves the toilet seat up). It reminds me of the way everyone in Roosevelt sweeps their sidewalks on Thursday nights.

My apartment might be tiny, but it has a lot to like. I would never have found it without Harold. It's in a great building (no bugs or vermin), and it is an easy walk to Barnard. It is quieter than the dorms, and a lot less expensive. I love walking down the hallway at night and smelling what everyone is cooking for dinner—garlic, bell peppers and onions; or ginger, basil and rosemary—a symphony of scents. I love hearing Mr. Mola singing Rigoletto while he cooks his rigatoni.

Yanina, writing this letter has got me day dreaming about our days together in Roosevelt. I am glad kibbutz life agrees with you. I am happy you and Simcha found each other. But I want to knock on the wall between our houses, step out on the porch and talk to you the way we used to. I want to stroll down Homestead Lane together and smell Mrs. Lachman's rosemary hedges.

Remember how we would loop onto Pine Drive and bask in the parade of roses from Mrs. Appel's to Mrs. Landau's, an entire street with roses in every yard, so many shades of red, pink and yellow. Remember how we danced down that street to Mr. Martin's music? Mr. Martin would see us dancing and he would say, "Zatańczy, you are true to your name. You will dance through your life." We would promenade along Tamara Drive and then turn left onto Rochdale with its vegetable gardens. (Bubba still talks about how they have better dirt in those gardens on Rochdale than anywhere else in Roosevelt.) Then we would turn back onto Homestead Lane and head home for a cup of tea.

And yes, now I remember finding that quote from Mrs. Roosevelt, "You gain strength, courage and confidence by every experience in which you stop to look in fear's face. You are able to say to yourself, I lived through this horror. I can take what next comes along." I remember finding Mama's copy of Mrs. Roosevelt's book, *You Learn by Living.* I sat down and devoured it without looking up. I kept repeating that quote for days. Bubba would hear me and say, "Struggle, hope. Two sides, one coin." Zayde would chime in, "For our lungs, oxygen; for life's meaning, hope. But hope is a good breakfast, but a bad supper." And we would ask him, "What's for lunch?" as we fell over each other giggling.

Mrs. Roosevelt has always been important in my life. I just didn't realize how important she was. I hope I can find a topic for my thesis in her letters, a topic that Smyth will approve.

Always,

Joan

Joan to Yanina

July 3, 1961

Dear Yanina,

I'm staying at Barnard this summer. I want to get ahead on my reading for next semester. And now I want to spend more time with Harold too. Thank you for the warning about Harold, but I trust him. Our night by the Cathedral was so wonderful. The stars were bright, and Harold was tender. We care about each other. What else matters? I am focusing on the sweetness of that night and not letting myself worry about other shoes dropping.

But, yesterday a different shoe dropped. I had a meeting with Harold for my senior audit, to go over the courses I need to graduate, and he was all Dr. Smyth. Yanina, I spent three years taking courses to meet all the college requirements. We met every semester to plan out my schedule. Sure, some semesters I dropped a course. But I always took that course or a similar one the next semester. It always seemed like a good idea when I dropped a course. I was not going to let anything break my streak of straight A's. The registrar's office lets you drop courses way after you can add replacements, so I thought it must be all right. I mean, I have all the college general curriculum classes finished. I am rounding in on finishing all the requirements for my history major. But Dr. Smyth looked at my transcript and then looked at me like I was dandruff on a black sweater.

I have been full time every semester. I thought if I was full time for four years, if I took all the general curriculum courses and finished my major requirements, I would graduate. How did I not know you have to take electives too! How did I not realize you also have to finish one hundred twenty four credits? I am so short of being anywhere near that number, I am dumbstruck. Smyth says I'm not even a senior yet. I'm still a junior. I trusted him to keep me on track for graduation. I hope there are not any other college rules he didn't tell me about.

That night at the Cathedral he was Harold to me, but through our whole meeting he was Dr. Smyth. He kept getting more and more frustrated with me. He kept scowling. He told me my butt was in a sling. No big eyes. No calling me Soigné. None of that. He said my best hope for graduating is December 1962. This May is not even a remote possibility. He sat there scowling, at me, at my transcript, at the fall schedule. Finally, after more scowling and scribbling notes, he said I should keep all the courses I am registered for in the fall. There was at least that. I was afraid he would tell me I had to switch out of Dr. Fredrick's philosophy course. Dr. Smyth says the course is a waste of time. But it looks interesting to me, and now that I need to take more electives, he said I might as well keep it. Dr. Smyth kept lecturing me about how I can never, not ever, drop another course. He also said I will need to add one more course. A new woman professor is teaching Women in History in the fall, and it fits in my schedule, so he said to add it as an elective.

I didn't mention the sack of letters to him. His frustration overwhelmed anything I had to say, and I was too overwhelmed to say anything. I couldn't bear him telling me another of my senior thesis topics wasn't good enough.

After our meeting, I came back to my apartment and reread some of Mrs. Roosevelt's letters to Mama to clear my head. I felt like there was a herd of butterflies trying to escape through my ears. As I was digging around in the bag, I found this letter about Mrs. Roosevelt's trip to the Gila Internment Camp. She sure didn't let herself get overwhelmed, not even by her husband, not even when he was the President of the United States. Once she made up her mind something was important, she plucked up her courage and gave it another go. I want to pluck up my courage and forge ahead the way she does. It would be so marvelous to meet her and talk with her.

Yanina, did you know we put our Japanese people into internment camps in the desert? I can't imagine the dust. (How dusty is your Negev Desert?) I can't imagine how those Japanese people did it. But they focused on *gaman*—to bear the unbearable with patience and dignity. But how did they manage dignity in all that dust? How did they keep anything clean?

After I read for a while and the butterflies in my head settled down, I took the train to Roosevelt. The entire way, I was dreading having to tell Mama and Aunt Stasia I will not graduate in May. Aunt Stasia always asked me if it was advisable to drop those courses. Now I have to tell her it was not.

During the train ride, I kept asking myself, "What would Mrs. Roosevelt do?" But she would never get into such an unholy mess in the first place. But, then I remembered those Japanese ladies and their gaman, their patience and dignity. I tried to think of a way to keep my dignity while I told Mama and Aunt Stasia.

Just as the train was pulling into the station, I remembered how Aunt Stasia taught us to tell people unpleasant news. Open with a roundabout story. Don't walk up to someone and say, "I found your dead cat laying in your front yard." Talk about how you love to see their cat playing. Then say you saw it walking along rain gutter on the edge of the roof, and it seemed a little unsteady. Pause and say the cat fell off the gutter as it wobbled. It looked so calm and peaceful when it fell, but it was not breathing. Aunt Stasia says as you tell the story, the person can prepare for a bad ending. (Aunt Stasia does love to tell a story. She still says a good story is like a twice baked potato, the more you retell it and add to it, the better it gets.)

After dinner, Mama asked me about my meeting with Dr. Smyth. I told her because it was a nice afternoon, we met on the porch roof of Withey Hall, I started musing about what it would be like to be a cat on a hot tin roof, but Dr. Smyth wasn't interested in my musings and needed the forms on his desk, so we went back into his office.

Aunt Stasia said she was relieved to hear we came in off the roof, but what was I building up to telling them? She said sometimes quickly ripping the Band-Aid off is better than leaving the cat dangling.

I took a deep breath and said we did my senior course audit. Mama and Aunt Stasia looked at me, at each other and said, "And?" I plunged on and told them I have completed eighty credits, and am registered for fifteen credits in the fall. I will take fifteen credits in the spring, which will bring me up to one hundred and ten. But I need one hundred twenty four to graduate. That is fourteen credits short, so I need an extra semester. I said I will get a job this summer and save up to cover the extra semester's costs. The Barnard Bulletin always has an ad for Kelly Girls. I can type 50 words a minute without mistakes. With practice, I am certain I can get up to 60 wpm. I admitted I messed up, but promised to make it right. I said that all in one breath while I was holding my breath. Oh, Yanina, what an idiot I am.

I stopped talking and there was a thundering silence. It was a silence as thick as split pea soup. It hung over the table like New York smog. We all just sat there. Eventually, Aunt Stasia asked me how my grades were. I reminded her I made the Dean's List every semester, I have straight A's in all my courses. She asked if I have been learning. I have. She launched into a soliloquy extolling the value and virtues of money spent on learning. She wrapped her speech up, saying we would find a way for the extra semester to happen without my taking on extra jobs. Mama scowled at Aunt Stasia, then at me. She kept scowling and said, "Joan, how could you." It was an accusation, not a question.

She sat there scowling, with her arms folded over her chest scratching her elbows the way she does and allowed as how my scholarship gives up to five years to complete an undergraduate degree as long as sufficient and continuous progress can be documented.

Mama can be so cold. I know she is kind more often than not, but there are times when she is just so cold. I was sitting there feeling like the world's prime disappointment. I needed a hug. But she droned on reciting the conditions of my scholarship. Sure that's important. But, even if I don't act like it most of the time, I have feelings too. I couldn't wait to go next door and pour my heart out to Zayde. The way he listens, everything gets easier. He is my anchor.

Yanina, how could I mess up so badly? I mean every semester on the Dean's List. How did I not take enough credits? I said that to Mama, and she looked at me with that look of hers, "Joan, you are as bright as they come. You may well be the brightest bulb in the pack, but practical details are not your strong suit. You may want to be a free spirit like your father, but discipline and focus are still important. Distinction is in the details."

Who is she talking about, saying I want to be a free spirit? I am the most focused, disciplined person in all of Roosevelt. Maybe I get too focused on some things and miss the irrelevant details. I guess maybe sometimes some of what I think is irrelevant might be important, but still, it's like she doesn't even know me. She doesn't see how hard I try to not be like my father.

But, one thing she is right about, "Distinction is in the details." I have to pay attention to all the details from now on. 'Details' reminds me of one of my favorite Ernest Hemingway quotes, "Everyone's life ends the same way. The details of how we live distinguish us from another."

Did you hear Hemingway died yesterday? I guess he won't be writing anymore novels.

Anyway, details—I better pay better attention to all of them all the time. But even Mrs. Roosevelt didn't always succeed on her first try. She tried to get her husband to change his mind about the Japanese people, but he proceeded with his Executive Order. After she visited that Japanese internment camp, she kept trying to get him to listen to her. So I will keep on working to complete all my requirements and all the credits I need to graduate. I have to get myself back on track.

Anyway, tomorrow is the 4th of July here. I can't wait for Roosevelt's parade and the Klassic Klezmer Kompetition.
What's your tale, Nightingale? How are my favorite Kibbutznicks doing?

Yours, always,

Joan

From Mrs. Roosevelt to Eva Zatańczy

April 30, 1943

Dear Eva,

I understand your confusion and concern regarding how our country is treating our Japanese people. You and I share those same concerns. On April 23, I made a journey to inspect the living conditions of the people in the Gila River Internment Camp, which is fifty miles southeast of Phoenix, Arizona. I was told that Gila is a model camp built to house persons of Japanese ancestry in commodious conditions. That is what I was told, but that is not what I saw.

As my motorcade approached the camp gate, the children's chorus began singing "America the Beautiful." I rolled down my window so they could see me smiling and waving. The camp administrators offered their greetings and then a small troop of boys and girls lined up in front of me. One boy, no older than 8 or 9, stepped forward, and in one breath, welcomed me to the "Gila River War Relocation Camp, within the Gila River Indian Reservation, which has two separate areas, the Butte and the Canal areas." Two girls, who were also 8 or 9, stepped forward, the first thrust a bouquet of lovely garden flowers at me, saying, "Welcome from the Butte Camp." The second girl all but tripped as she thrust her bouquet at me saying, "Welcome from the Canal Camp."

That near trip set off a ripple of giggles among the children, scowls from their teacher, and smiles among the mothers. It was a lovely greeting, a gift of remarkable generosity from people my husband had summarily arrested and taken from their jobs and homes to the dry, dusty Arizona desert. It touched my heart deeply.

After the official greetings we toured the camp and inspected the communal kitchens, dining area, laundry, school, recreational hall and the factories. The internees themselves built many of these facilities. They have also arranged their own police force, fire department and town government. The people interned in Gila demonstrated remarkable resilience and grit.

As we walked to the housing area, I asked my guides, Mrs. Ishida and Mrs. Fujisawa, about their experiences when they were brought to Gila. Tears came to their eyes as they told me how government men came to their homes, arrested their husbands and took them away in handcuffs. When the women asked what their husbands had done, they were brusquely told to be quiet or they too would be arrested. The following day the women were told they and their families had three days to gather their possessions—they could only bring what they could carry—and to dispose of the rest. They were to report to relocation centers, where some women, children and grandparents were reunited with their husbands, fathers and sons. Families were boarded on trains and then busses and taken to relocation camps away from the west coast. Most of the families at Gila are second generation citizens of this country.

I was furious when I saw how we are treating our own people. I was furious with Franklin for executing that order. Eva, these are things I must never say in public, but that does not mean I do not feel them in my heart.

Franklin and I often disagree on how to best address the needs of the people of our great country. I speak my point of view to him as emphatically as possible, but Franklin is his own man, and he follows his own mind. The American people elected Franklin, and not I, as their president. But that does not stop me from energetically making my point of view known. After the attack on Pearl Harbor, when it came to arresting and relocating persons of Japanese ancestry, my point of view did not carry the day. But now I have talked to people who were relocated, and I have seen the conditions they are living in. Now my point of view will be heard.

The women told me army recruiters came to the camp to ask for volunteers. The recruiters were particularly interested in men who could read, write and speak Japanese. Mrs. Fujisawa said many of the young men in the camp volunteered for the army. For them, it was a way to demonstrate their loyalty to the country, and to prove Executive Order 9066 was not only unfair but also unjust. She apologized to me for saying this concerning the Executive Order and said their sons were young and meant no disrespect to my husband, the president. I assured her no disrespect was taken, and that I could understand their sons' point of view.

Eva, what I wanted to say was I that agreed with their sons' point of view, but I have learned that when I am on an official inspection trip, I must be circumspect in my public comments.

As we walked to the barracks, I learned the Gila River Camp was built to hold 10,000 people. There are currently 14,000 people there. Families are assigned to an apartment twenty feet by twenty feet. Four hundred square feet, divided into a kitchen, living room and bedrooms for the entire family. Mothers, fathers, children, grandparents, aunts, uncles and cousins, all in one apartment.

Mrs. Ishida and Mrs. Fujisawa were proud to show me their apartments. Their creativity transformed that Spartan space into a warm and homey abode. I commented to Mrs. Ishida that the room was not as hot as I might have expected. She told me the buildings have a double roof to help keep out the heat, and that is important, because summer temperatures reach 125 degrees. I noticed a beautiful Japanese calligraphy on a wall behind a table with statues and pictures of family members. I asked Mrs. Ishida about it. She told me *gaman* is a Buddhist word. In English it means bearing the unbearable with patience and dignity. She said it reminds her family to persevere with dignity, even, especially, in this place. Imagine, Eva, patience, perseverance and dignity, in the middle of all the degradation our government has imposed on these families.

We left the barracks area and walked over to see the baseball field the families built, and then to the outdoor theater where the children put on a concert for me, singing patriotic American songs and traditional Japanese songs. The Japanese music was beautiful, light and haunting. Mrs. Fujisawa told me the song the youngest girls danced to is called the Happy Dolls song. She translated for me as the children sang:

Let us light the lanterns

Let us gather peach blossoms
Play the flutes and drums
Today is Happy Dolls Festival.

Mrs. Fujisawa said the children sang that song in my honor, because my visit made their dolls happy. Their joyful concert was a balm for my anger with Franklin.

How bittersweet that trip was. I was delighted to meet the people and profoundly saddened and angered to bear witness to what our government has done to its loyal citizens.

Eva, my trip has strengthened my resolve to persuade Franklin to reconsider his Executive Order 9066. The people I met at the Gila River Camp are proud American citizens who love our country. Some of them are resentful of the way our government treated them, but when you look at what has happened to them, I would be concerned if they were not. Above everything else, the families at the Gila River Camp are people who want their lives back and their freedom returned.

They walk and live with gaman, knowing their old lives are over and they have no homes to return to, but eager to dust themselves off and start over, to build new lives. Such a lot of dust to be brushed off. The Arizona desert where we have moved these people is one of the dustiest places I have ever been.

After this visit, I am even more determined that every American should enjoy the same basic freedoms. Every citizen of this great country of ours has an equal right to dignity, justice and equal opportunities. We can no longer afford the wrong minded extravagance of looking at any group who might be different as less than any other group. Our country was not built by a common race, but on common values. Our men are at war to preserve our democratic way of life. The least we can do at home is to strive to live up to the ideas and ideals of democracy.

Eva, I have gone on more than I intended here. But, I am wondering how you are. Do tell me the latest news concerning you dear Joan and Bronislaw? When my children were young, I relied on my mother-in-law and the help we had to keep up with day-to-day tasks. As I travel the country now serving as Franklin's eyes and ears I am learning how fortunate and privileged we were. I think about you on your own caring for young Joan while Bronislaw is off fighting. So many mothers across the country are on their own while their husbands and sons are at war.

Even in these trying times, I continue to learn the importance of perspective, and of aspiration, imagination and determination. I have recently finished reading a wonderful new book by Betty Smith, "A Tree Grows in Brooklyn" which tells the story of Francie Nolan and her family. Their immigration experience stands in stark contrast to how we are treating our Japanese citizens. When will we ever learn? No matter how different we may look, all people are human beings.

At our core, we are the same. When will we ever learn?

What is the news in your Jersey Homesteads? How are your daughter and husband, and the ladies of your sewing circle?

With love, your affectionate friend,

Eleanor

Joan to Yanina

August 7, 1961

Dear Yanina,

Man-oh-Manischewitz. The other shoe has dropped but good. I'm up Schits Creek in a barbed wire canoe with no paddle! First, I'm not graduating on time. Now Harold keeps giving me grief about my thesis. He is totally being Dr. Smyth. Our night by the Cathedral changed things between us, but not the way I hoped. He used to be my friend. Now he is too busy to spend any time with me. It's like he got what he wanted, and he is done with me!

And when I ask him about his trip to Stanford, he looks like he ate a wasp, and says, "Don't bug me." He has become Dr. Jekyll and Mr. Hyde, except he is being totally Mr. Hyde.
What is it with him? I told him about the letters from Mrs. Roosevelt and how I want to use them to analyze her contributions to drafting the United Nations *Universal Declaration of Human Rights*. The United Nations *Universal Declaration of Human Rights*—one of the most important documents of the century. Mrs. Roosevelt was at the heart of getting it written and ratified, and I have a whole sack of letters from Mrs. Roosevelt about her work at the United Nations. What could be more perfect?

But no. "Too recent, too personal, not authenticated, not enough emotional distance, not enough objectivity." Too much this, not enough that. But I stood my ground with him. I remembered gaman. And I remembered the letter Mrs. Roosevelt wrote when she was on her way to her first United Nations meeting. (I'm sending you a copy with this letter.) Mrs. Roosevelt wrote about Mercy Otis Warren and Abigail Adams and how they stood their ground throughout the American Revolution. Women have been standing their ground for a long time, I finally stood my ground with Dr. Smyth. We debated point after point until he said, maybe.
But I have to get official permission from Mama and Mrs. Roosevelt. And I have to have supporting primary sources. What could be more primary than letters from Mrs. Roosevelt?

But they are too personal. If they had been written to anyone other than my mother that would have been fine. If I found them in the corner of someone's attic, or in a garage sale, that would have been fine. But because they were written to my mother, that is too personal. I need primary sources where I have more objectivity. And he wants confirmation of the provenance of the letters. Provenance, providence, predominance, why is he being so rigid and uptight?
I will get permission from Mama and Mrs. Roosevelt. And I will find additional supporting primary sources. I am curious to see what else I might learn about Mrs. Roosevelt and her work at the United Nations. I have to meet her and talk with her now that I have read all these letters.

Yanina, part of me feels battered and beaten down. But there is another part of me that is even more determined. I will not let Smyth push me around with this. I have finally found a topic for my senior thesis that captures my interest and passion. I'm bound and determined I will attend to every detail and write the best senior thesis anyone at Barnard ever wrote.

After my meeting with Smyth I kept repeating what Mercy Otis Warren said, "The waves have rolled upon me, the billows are repeatedly broken over me, yet I am not sunk down." I am not sunk down. I will get my topic approved. I will graduate. I will not falter.

Yanina, I keep rereading Mrs. Roosevelt's letter from when she worked at the United Nations. She was over 60 years old by then. I just turned 21. I still have time to figure out what to do with my life after I graduate. I want to learn more about the women she writes about in her letters. I hope I will learn more about women like that in Women in History next semester. I hope that new professor is good. I hope . . .
Oh, let me stop. Mrs. Roosevelt would say, "Great minds discuss ideas; average minds discuss events; small minds discuss people."

From now on, it's ideas for me.

Mama has already given me her official written permission. And, when I was home to ask Mama to sign the Barnard forms, I got Aunt Stasia alone for a minute and asked her how Mama started to write to Mrs. Roosevelt. But Mama walked in on us, and Aunt Stasia said, "Later." But then I had to get the train.

After I finish writing this letter, I will write to Mrs. Roosevelt and ask her for permission to use the letters and to confirm the provenance of the letters. I hope Mrs. Roosevelt can suggest another primary source for her work at the United Nations.

Why do things have to be so complicated? I keep searching for meaning and purpose, but all I find are delays and detours.

Oh, and I have an appointment with health services tomorrow. I wake up every morning with an upset stomach from worrying about senior thesis stuff and the way Smyth has treating me. I'm so frustrated with him.

Yanina, life on your kibbutz sounds amazing. I love your description of Ariadne. Tanned, wiry, always in a blue shirt, rolled up khaki shorts and sandals, practical, no nonsense and a heart as big as the Negev desert. I hope I get to meet her someday. Tell me more about the joys of kibbutz life.
Do you really want me to keep sending bag letters to you?

Always,

Joan

From ER to Eva

December 31, 1945

Dear Eva,

Only eight months ago I was burying my Franklin and thinking my life in public affairs was at its end. And now President Truman has invited me to serve as one of the United States Delegates to the United Nations.

Eva, I must confess my instinct was to decline. I felt I did not know enough concerning international matters, that I had nothing to offer. But conversations with family and friends helped me to see things differently. I agreed to accept the invitation.

Now, it is New Year's Eve, and I am aboard the Queen Elizabeth, sailing for South Hampton, England. From there we will travel on to London and the inaugural sessions of the United Nations. As we sail, I still wonder what I might have to contribute to the meetings. Self-doubt can be haunting and harrowing. In this school of life, I am constantly learning to face my doubts head on, and to confront at least one thing that frightens me each day. Most days there is no shortage of fears to confront.

Earlier today as I was reflecting on my fears and self-doubts, I remembered the "My Day" column I wrote 10 days ago. In that column I listed some things I take to my work at the United Nations: a sincere desire to understand the problems of the rest of the world and our relationship to them; goodwill for people throughout the world; and hope that I shall be able to build a sense of personal trust and friendship with my coworkers. Now I must remember these qualities and carry them with me as I begin this work.

Eva, as I reflected on these things last night, I wondered what doubts the founding mothers of our country might have experienced. I remembered Mercy Otis Warren, and I wondered what life was like for her when our country was a collection of colonies in the British Empire. To wonder, dream and imagine are not so different. I wonder about something and imagine how it might have been, day dreaming the details.

Are you familiar with Mercy Otis Warren and her brother? Mercy's brother, James Otis was the first fellow to shout out "Taxation without representation is tyranny." That sentiment helped to foment the ideas and ideals that fueled the colonies' revolution from the British Empire. Mrs. Warren was close friends with Abigail and her husband John Adams. John Adams in particular encouraged Mrs. Warren to write.

As early as 1772, Mercy was writing plays describing the struggles in the colonies against the British. Her writing was vital in helping to build and strengthen opposition to the British within the colonies, so much so she became known as the Muse of the Revolution. As with many women, she was invisible in her efforts, but her efforts had an important effect.
Far too often the contributions of women are forgotten or rendered invisible.

I remember a story about a day in 1777 when the British attacked Danbury, Connecticut. A messenger arrived at the home of Henry Ludington to warn him and to have him gather the militia. But his men were disbursed, working on their farms. Henry needed to stay at home to muster the men as they arrived. His oldest daughter, Sybil, only 16, volunteered to rouse the men from their farm work. At 9 PM she set out, riding 20 miles on horseback through a thunderstorm, shouting "Gather at Ludington's, the British are burning Danbury." Sybil was half the age of Paul Revere and rode twice as far, but history remembers the man and neglects the girl.

Abigail Adams told her husband John to remember the ladies. He failed to listen, but the ladies keep on working, for our country and for our rights. I can hear Mercy calling out to the women of today, "The waves have rolled upon me, the billows are repeatedly broken over me, yet I am not sunk down."

The men in Philadelphia wrote a constitution for our nascent nation that neglected state's rights, favored the aristocracy over democracy, and quashed women's voice, vote and role in governing. But Mercy Otis Warren kept writing and challenging them to do better, her words helped to shape the Bill of Rights. Mercy called for "a heroic love for the public good, a profound reverence for the laws, a contempt of riches, and a noble haughtiness of the soul" as the foundations of a free government.

Oh, Eva, people seem to cultivate haughtiness of the ego, and lose sight of the nobility of the soul and spirit. We might celebrate our fighting spirit, but nobility of the spirit seems lost in our world. That is a loss we can ill afford.

This morning I woke up thinking nobility of soul and spirit is something the new United Nations must affirm and promote.

Mercy Otis Warren was clear that the powers of the government and those who govern need to be explicitly limited. She called for a Bill of Rights to guard against the encroachments of power into the rights, liberties and freedoms of the people. As we work to build the new United Nations, I believe we will need a Bill of Rights to protect the rights, liberties and freedoms of the peoples of the world. Rights and responsibilities are two sides of the same coin, both will need to be detailed. There is much work to be done if this new United Nations is to be effective in its work for peace.

The lives and work of Mercy Otis Warren and Abigail Adams challenge me to have confidence in myself. Women have had input into policy and governance, but not the recognition. Now my generation of women has a chance to be recognized for our work. We cannot squander that opportunity.

We stand on the shoulders of those before us. We must remember their accomplishments. We must stand tall and walk into our future with ever greater strength and dignity even as we remember the sacrifices and contributions of those who have gone before us.

My Dear Eva, it has now been more than a year since your dear Bronislaw was killed in the war. Life is moving so quickly. Even while we grieve, we must find a way to carry on, to take up our lives. How did your young Joan like the first half of kindergarten? Are you still enjoying working as a secretary in the Roosevelt School? I can just picture Joan and her new friend Yanina asserting their independence and insisting on walking home on their own. The urge for independence does come early in our young ones. I am so pleased that you have your sister-in-law Anastasia there with you to help.

With love, your affectionate friend,

Eleanor

Joan Zatańczy at Barnard College New York City to Mrs. Eleanor Roosevelt at Hyde Park, New York

August 7, 1961

Dear Mrs. Roosevelt,

Your letters to my Mama are the best present Mama ever gave me. I cannot tell you how many times I have poured over those letters. Every time I read them I learn something new. I never realized the depth and breadth of women's contributions to making our world a better place. Women have a long history of fighting for our rights and working to make the world a better place. That history should be recognized and celebrated!

Your letters have inspired me to reconsider how I want to live my life. For Mama, being competent, knowing how to do what you need to do to get through the day, is the most important thing. Aunt Stasia says being awake and aware is what is most important, but to me she seems to be all about being a good person who is kind to others. But when I read your letters, I see women with bigger dreams and visions; I see women of strength committed to making our world better.

Now I am spending all my free time reading about the women you mention in your letters, and next semester I am taking a course called Women in History where I hope to learn even more about women who made a difference in our world.

I am inspired by the work that you did at the United Nations, by your thoughtfulness, determination and skill. I hope I can learn to emulate your resolve and fortitude.

Mrs. Roosevelt, I am writing to thank you for all the ways you inspire me, and also to ask you a favor.

I am starting my senior year at Barnard College and I need to find a topic for my senior thesis for my history degree. I would like to use your letters to Mama for my project. My topic would be "Mrs. Eleanor Roosevelt and the United Nations *Universal Declaration of Human Rights*." But my professor, Dr. Smyth, is being an obstructionist. He says he will only allow me to use the letters if both you and Mama sign the Barnard College Research Consent Form and if you confirm the provenance of the letters. Dr. Smyth wants you to confirm in writing that you wrote those letters to my Mama—that I did not concoct this like some kind of crazy story.

I don't mean to be forward, but I have included a copy of the Barnard form with this letter. I am hoping you might sign it and give me permission to use your letters for my senior thesis project, please?

Also, I am sorry to be asking you all of this, but Dr. Smyth says that besides the letters between you and Mama, I need to have additional primary sources. Mama thought you would know where I could find other sources related to your work at the United Nations? Dr. Smyth says then the letters from you to Mama could be part of my research, like a case study.

So, please, Mrs. Roosevelt, will you give me your permission?

Thank you for all you have done to help people around the world, and to help my family.

Sincerely,

Joan Zatańczy

# *Part II*
# *Fall Semester 1961*

Joan to Yanina

September 5, 1961

Dear Yanina,

I'm pregnant. How can I be pregnant? I mean, know how it happened. But Yanina, once. Only once. No one gets pregnant the first time they have sex!

Remember I said my stomach was so upset? I went to the health clinic at school and they did all kinds of tests. The results came in and the nurse told me I was pregnant. I must have passed out because the next thing I knew, I was on the exam table and three nurses and a doctor where hovering around me. The nurse who told me I was pregnant said, "I guess you didn't suspect you were expecting?" I absolutely did not.

It took me a day to collect the pieces of my discombobulated self and gather up the few remaining shreds of my courage. Then I made the trek to Roosevelt to tell Mama and Aunt Stasia. They took one look at me and knew something was wrong. We sat in the kitchen, Aunt Stasia made us some tea, and I told them. They both said, "Joan, no," at the same time. Mama sat there rocking back and forth in her chair crying, saying, "Oh no," over and over again. She said, "What will the Steins say? What will the sewing circle say? We can never show our faces in town again. We will have to leave Roosevelt. But that would cost us your Roosevelt Scholarship."

Aunt Stasia got all Zen, looked Mama square in the eyes and said, "Eva, we will stay where we are. Roosevelt has never been orthodox. Everyone here has something hidden in their closet. Everyone in this town has their secrets. We will stay where we are. We will continue to be proud of our Joan. We will be proud of our grandchild, and we will love them both."

Aunt Stasia never talks to Mama like that. Mama started to get up from the table, but she collapsed into her chair crying. She said, "Joan, you will finish college, however long it takes, you will finish. Whatever you decide to do about this mess you have gotten yourself into, I will not let you waste that opportunity."

More crying. More "Oh, Joan."

Aunt Stasia and Mama looked at me and said, "Joan." They looked at each other. Mama asked me, "How? How did this happen?" I told them the Cathedral story. More "Oh, Joan."

Aunt Stasia said they will help me, whatever I decide to do, but Mama kept looking at me like I was a bag of flaming dog poop someone left at the front door on Halloween night.
Once I got back to Barnard, I called Harold. He tried to say the baby wasn't his. But I told him it couldn't belong to anyone else; our time by the Cathedral was my only time. Finally he said he would do the right thing. Only Harold's doing the right thing was arranging for an abortion. Of course, abortions aren't legal, but, he said he knew someone who knew a doctor. I never saw anyone make phone calls so fast.

The doctor was nice enough. His office, if you can call it that, is a room above a Greek restaurant a few blocks from Barnard. It was clean, with a sink, stool and examination table—that's all there was space for. The doctor sent Harold out of the room, as much because the three of us couldn't fit in the room, as for my privacy. We talked a little, then he examined me and said my due date is early February. He explained my options: abortion, adoption or acquiescence (which means keeping the baby). He was ready to schedule the abortion for next week. As if I could just decide right then and there!

I took a deep breath to clear my head, and I almost wretched from the smell of garlic from the restaurant downstairs. I'm supposed to call him and tell him what I want to do. Whatever I do, I will not let Harold push me into doing something I don't want to do.

On our way back to Barnard, Harold told me he is moving to Stanford for the spring semester. They offered him a faculty position, and he has accepted it. Basically he said, "Good luck and goodbye."

I trusted him. I thought he was my friend. I know it was only once between us, but we have been friends since he was my freshman advisor. I thought we were becoming more. I believed all the things he said. I was a fool. Mama is right, never trust a promise. I should have known better than to trust him. After this, I will know better than to trust anyone.
I am pregnant and I am on my own. I don't know what I will do, but I do know I will not let Harold will not get off that easy. If I'm in a mess, so is he.

Should I consider adoption? But how could I give my baby to a stranger? Would that be better for the baby? Yanina, my head is spinning. I don't know how to think about this. There are days when all I can do is sit and cry. This is so not me. I'm good at analyzing things, making a plan, and jumping in with both feet. But everything is spinning so fast, I can't think. I can't find the ground under my feet. I can't even find my feet.

The semester starts tomorrow. I need to get my head into school and classes, but the only thing circling in my head is how stupid I am. I was the smartest kid in high school. I was pronounced the queen of reason and discipline in our yearbook. And now I'm not graduating on time, I'm pregnant, and Harold, my baby's father, says he is doing the right thing by taking me to a doctor who will perform an illegal abortion. But, I don't know if I want to have an abortion. What if even half that stuff we read about the dangers and risks of abortions are true? What if something goes wrong?

I wish this could be like when I was 10 and got lost in Assunpink Park. Those woods were so scary, and I was so lost. Then Zayde was calling my name. He found me, and rescued me. But no one can rescue me from this.

Mama is right, nothing good ever comes from being wild and free. Nothing good ever comes from believing promises. I am too much like my Papa. Even if I never knew him, I must have inherited his trusting, free spirit. I have to be more self-sufficient, focused and disciplined.

All of this emotion, being confused and scared and trying to think and figure out what to do, I feel like I am stuck in the spin cycle of an out-of-control clothes washer. Being rational and living in my head is so much calmer. Rereading Mrs. Roosevelt's letters has become my refuge. I was rereading her "Elizabeth Cady Stanton and the Seneca Falls Convention" letter, and when I reread the passages Mrs. Roosevelt quoted from the Declaration of Sentiments from the convention, I wanted to throw something (so much for being calm).

They wrote that Declaration one hundred thirteen years ago, and women are still second-class citizens. Sure we got the right to vote. But men are still running things and pushing women around and getting away with their mistakes. Look at how Smyth thinks he can just walk away from me even though I am pregnant with his baby. I have to find a way to hold him accountable. I have to decide what to do.

Yanina, parts of kibbutz life may be frustrating, but you are still living your dream. For me, everything is falling apart. George Bernard Shaw said "life is a flame that is always burning itself out, but it catches fire again every time a child is born."

All I see is smoke and ashes. My life is going up in smoke and ashes.

Always,

Joan

From ER to Eva

May 1, 1946

Dear Eva,

The work to build the United Nations continues apace. The pace is brisk in some respects and slow as molasses in others. But, any progress is splendid news. One major development has been the creation of a Nuclear Commission which will recommend to the General Assembly the parameters of structure and function for a permanent Commission of Human Rights. The General Assembly appointed nine of its members to the committee. I am honored to be included among the nine. I am the only woman in the group, but my colleagues have chosen me chair the committee.

This work evokes many of my old fears and insecurities. How those old ghosts haunt me. But, I remember my father's belief that I was his brave girl, I marshal my courage and forge my way forward. Many nights as I wait for deep sleep to carry me off, I imagine what it was like for the brave women whose efforts helped to create the opportunities that are now open to you and I.

Last night as I lay in bed in that numinous place between waking and sleep, I was reflecting on the work of Miss Elizabeth Cady Stanton and the women of Seneca Falls who produced the Declaration of Rights and Sentiments in 1848, nearly 100 years ago.

I imagined what it would have been like for Miss Stanton at the Women's Rights Convention at Seneca Falls. Before the sessions opened on July 19, she received a letter of encouragement from Sarah Grimke, who could not attend the Convention, but was as an active supporter of women's rights. Sarah wrote, "We shall ask no favors for our sex. Neither shall we surrender our claims to equality. All we as of our brethren is that they take their feet off from our necks and permit us to stand upright on that ground which God intended us to occupy."

Before the Women's Rights Convention adopted the Declaration of Rights and Sentiments, Miss Stanton and Miss Mott read it aloud to the group, pausing for discussion at the end of each paragraph, because many of the women could not read, and it would have been an unfairness to the women to ask them to vote on a document without their having full knowledge of its contents. (I think this would be a useful practice for our Congress to take up as they consider legislation. It might change a thing or two in Washington.)

Eva, imagine being in that room and hearing Miss Stanton and Miss Lucretia Mott taking turns reading the declaration.

I imagined Miss Stanton's joy at the vote, even as she remembered the work done in the days, weeks and months preceding the convention in preparation for the meeting. Indeed, progress and success build on and flow from the good will of human relationships.

Eva, did you know they based the Declaration of Rights and Sentiments on the United States Declaration of Independence from England? Both build on the assertion of truths that are self-evident. Both articulate inalienable rights. Both discuss the relationship of the governed to their government. The Declaration of Sentiments is one of the earliest and most forceful efforts to articulate civil, political, social and religious rights for women.

The Declaration of Rights and Sentiments caused a good bit of uproar and controversy in its day. I think it should be more widely read and revered as one of our country's cherished documents. So many changes have come into our lives since they wrote it. We have accomplished much, yet much remains to be achieved. Here are a few passages from the Declaration that I find particularly inspiring.

We hold these truths to be self-evident: that all men and women are created equal; that they are endowed by their Creator with certain inalienable rights; among these are life, liberty and the pursuit of happiness; that to secure these rights governments are instituted, deriving their just powers from the consent of the governed.

Whenever any form of government becomes destructive of these ends, it is the right of those who suffer from it to refuse allegiance and to insist upon the institution of a new government . . . Prudence, indeed, will dictate that governments long established should not be changed for light and transient causes . . . but when a long train of abuses and usurpations, pursuing invariably the same object, evinces a design to reduce them under absolute despotism, it is their duty to throw off such government, and to provide new guards for their future security.

Such has been the patient sufferance of the women under this government, and such is now the necessity which constrains them to demand the equal station to which they are entitled.
The history of mankind is a history of repeated injuries and usurpations on the part of man toward woman, having in direct object the establishment of an absolute tyranny over her.

To prove this, let facts be submitted to a candid world.

He has never permitted her to exercise her inalienable right to the elective franchise.

He has compelled her to submit to laws, in the formation of which she had no voice.

Having deprived her of this first right of a citizen, the elective franchise, thereby leaving her without representation in the halls of legislation, he has oppressed her on all sides.
The Declaration of Sentiments details the practices men of their age engaged in which contributed to the oppression of women: denying them property rights, limiting their moral authority, giving husbands ownership of their wives, constraining the educational and employment opportunities and options available to women, defining women as lesser in every conceivable way before government, god and man.

The Declaration of Sentiments asserted that these oppressive practices destroyed women's confidence in their powers, lessened their self-respect, and compelled them to lead dependent and abject lives.

And it concludes:

"Now, in view of this entire disfranchisement of one-half the people of this country, their social and religious degradation, in view of the unjust laws above mentioned, and because women feel themselves aggrieved, oppressed, and fraudulently deprived of their most sacred rights, we insist that they have immediate admission to all the rights and privileges which belong to them as citizens of these United States."

I have no doubts that our work at the United Nations will encounter challenges. But, I am inspired by the work of the women who have gone before me. Good works require hard work, so work we will.

Dearest Eva, your last letter brought me some delightful moment of much needed mirth. Your Joan has become quite the handful. I do so enjoy reading your stories of her escapades.

With love, your affectionate friend,

Eleanor

Joan to Yanina

September 8, 1961

Dear Yanina,

I've been crying about being pregnant. I've been moaning about how the world is conspiring against me, about how my dreams are being crushed. I've been pacing the floor trying to think and failing miserably. I have been wailing about how being pregnant crushes my quest to do something important, to find the meaning of my life.

Then I took a breath and thought about Mrs. Roosevelt's letters. She didn't let circumstances stop her. She took what was in front of her, learned from it, and made it part of her life work. She gave birth to six children. Being pregnant will not crush my quest. I will make it the culmination of my quest. Raising a child to be a whole and happy human being is important. I will love my baby fully and completely. Having my baby, loving that baby for all I am worth, teaching her to be a strong and independent woman—that will be the meaning and purpose of my life.

Am I really thinking like this? What happened to the disciplined, reasoned and rational thinker who was going to change the world? She has found her purpose in life. I will change the world one person at a time. I will be an amazing mother. That will be the meaning of my life.

Now, I have to figure out how support the baby and myself. I might drop out of school and get a job. I could finish this semester, then I will only have two more semesters to finish later.

Somehow I will keep this little one and build a life for us.

So, that's what I've decided. I had to write and tell you before I change my mind.

Always,

Joan

Joan to Yanina

September 12, 1961

Dear Yanina,

Finally, the first day of Dr. Cobbe's Women in History class. I was so consumed with being pregnant, I lost track of looking forward to starting class. But finally I was sitting in the first row, fifteen minutes early, right in front of the teacher's desk, my regular spot in every class in every course I take. I looked around and recognized some girls from around campus. They all chatted aimlessly about who did what during summer vacation while we waited for class to start. I mostly listened. I was not going to say, "Oh I got pregnant by a faculty member who is now abandoning me with the baby."

Not when I am trying so hard to not look fat and pregnant. I am trying to just look fat.

Dr. Cobbe walked in ten minutes early, introduced herself and joined in the conversation. She said she was looking forward to teaching at Barnard and to learning along with us.
A professor saying she would learn along with us? I am not sure about that. I want my teachers to already know about what they are teaching.

Five minutes before class was scheduled to begin, Dr. Cobbe had us rearrange the chairs into a circle so everyone could see each other. Weird. But we moved thirteen chairs into a circle.

Twelve of us are taking the course, eight women and four men. Four men. More weirdness. Barnard is a women's college. This is a course on Women in History. What are guys doing intruding in our class? But they are. We can take courses at Columbia, I guess Columbia students can take courses at Barnard. Anyway, they are in the course for better or worse.

The other students in the class are a cast of characters. Next to me was a girl wearing a denim skirt and a tee shirt with, "If I Had a Hammer" written on it. I hope it is that she just likes the song.

An older Black woman sat next to tee shirt woman, then a classic Barnard looking coed, then a blond woman who looked like a beatnik in her purple head band, black turtleneck and black skirt; and then an unobtrusive, mousey little woman who looked like she should still be in high school.

The women sat together, and the guys clustered in their own little knot. The first guy sat next to mousey woman, and looking at him, he could be her brother; next was a fellow who could be a walking add from Brooks Brothers; then an artsy looking guy; and last was a sort of average looking guy. I mean there is nothing about him to notice, except maybe his tan. He's the kind of guy you could bump into in a store, apologize to him, and ten minutes later not even remember he was there. Except he is kind of cute in a way.

Next to the guys was a woman wearing a crazy wild print shirt and skirt, neither of which matched, neither of which had a prayer of ever matching up with anything else. I guess she might as well be wearing them together as not. The last woman was the most nerdiest looking person I have ever seen. She even had a plastic pocket protector tucked into her white oxford shirt pocket, with pens and a little slide rule tucked into it.

Precisely at ten, Dr. Cobbe stood up, cleared her throat, and we were off. She reviewed course assignments, describing each one, telling us what she expected from us. Then she sat down between the nerdy woman and me, looked each student in the eye and said, "Young Scholars, I hope this course will be a stimulating learning experience for you. I will do my best to ensure the course is both interesting and engaging. I expect each of you to do your best. I am here to help you with the work. Use my office hours to ask questions you have pertaining to the course and the assignments. I want this to be an engaging learning experience. At the same time, let me caution you, do not mistake my softness of style for softness of standards. I expect you to do your best to achieve excellence. Effort is necessary but not sufficient. Excellence is the goal. Grades will be based on the quality of your products, not on the quantity of effort you believe you expended."

"Excellence is the goal." She really put it out there.

After her explanations, Dr. Cobbe asked us to introduce ourselves with the usual: name, what year we are (junior, senior, like that), and to name two women who are special in our lives, one dead and one living, but no relatives. She said to name the dead woman first because this is a course on women in history. We were supposed to say one thing we admired about each woman and to limit our admiration to one sentence because we have a lot of ground to cover today.
My living woman could only be Eleanor Roosevelt. No question, it had to be her. As I was thinking about whom to choose for my dead woman, I remembered the letter I just sent to you.

I volunteered to start.

"Elizabeth Cady Stanton, who wrote the Declaration of Rights and Sentiments and claimed women's right to vote. Eleanor Roosevelt is a living woman I admire, because of her work with the United Nations and for human rights."

We went around the circle, and the other students named some impressive women too. I became a note taking maniac, trying to write the names of the women along with something about each of them. Get ready, Yanina. Behold the women who are special to our class.

After me, T-shirt woman named Joan of Arc, who cut her hair short, dressed in men's uniforms and led the French to victory over the English in the Battle of Orleans; (One of the guys winked at me when T-shirt woman named Joan of Arc. I wonder what that was about). She also named Alice Paul who started as a leader in the United States suffrage movement, now she is working to get Congress to pass a women's Equal Rights Amendment to the constitution.

Then Mary McLeod Bethune was named. She was a champion for the education of Negro girls, founder of the National Council of Negro Women, and a leader in advancing interracial understanding. (Did you know Mary McLeod Bethune and Eleanor Roosevelt were good friends?) Ella Josephine Baker who is an advocate for Black civil rights and human rights was also named.

Yanina, that reminds me. In her "My Day" Column yesterday Mrs. Roosevelt mentioned Preston Cobb, a 15-year-old Negro boy from Georgia, convicted of murder by an all-white jury. They sentenced him to death even though he is only a kid! Mrs. Roosevelt wants everyone to write to the governor of Georgia, Mr. Ernest Vandiver and ask him to grant Preston clemency. I will write a letter as soon as I finish writing this one to you. Would you write a letter too? A letter coming all the way from Israel would be something.

Back to class, that classic Barnard coed named Emma Goldman, an anarchist and all around trouble maker who worked for birth control and women's rights, and Lucy Burns who worked with Alice Paul to co-founded the National Woman's Party.

I guess I'm not the only one who knows about women in history.

Then came Susan B. Anthony an abolitionist and suffragette; and Del Martin and Phyllis Lyon co-founders of the Daughters of Bilitis (DOB) in San Francisco, the first social and political organization for lesbians in the United States. The class went silent when Beatnik Girl said 'lesbian.' I wrinkled my nose, and she glared at me. That Beatnik Girl gives me the willies.

Dr. Cobbe thanked her for naming women who had made important contributions to our world, what she said to each of us, then she looked at the student sitting next to Beatnik Girl, who named Ida B. Wells-Barnett, co-founder of the National Association for the Advancement of Colored People (NAACP), and a journalist who chronicled and denounced the lynching of Black people in the South; and Bella Abzug, a lawyer in New York City and an advocate for civil rights and peace, who wears wide-brimmed hats, so she is not mistaken for a secretary.

I was waiting to see how the guys would manage, but they held their own.

The first guy surprised me when he named Louisa May Alcott, the author of *Little Women* and one of the first authors to write specifically for girls. I wondered how a guy would even know about her. He also named Pearl S. Buck, the daughter of missionaries to China, who writes novels about American and Asian culture and is the first woman to win the Nobel Prize for Literature.

The man from Brooks Brothers named Harriet Tubman who was born a slave and became a conductor on the Underground Railroad, helping other runaway slaves to get to free northern states; and Rosa Parks, born in Montgomery Alabama, a leader in the Black civil rights movement, in 1955 she refused to give up her bus seat to a white person which led to a huge bus strike that challenged racial segregation practices. I would never have pegged him for someone who knew anything about civil rights but, there he was.

Artsy Guy named Julia Ward Howe, who wrote the Battle Hymn of the Republic, and was a poet and social activist; and Marian Anderson, an African-American contralto, one of the most celebrated singers of the twentieth century. The Daughters of the American Revolution (DAR) refused permission for Anderson to sing to an integrated audience in Constitution Hall, so Eleanor Roosevelt arranged for her to perform at the Lincoln Memorial.

The last guy named Sappho, a Greek poet from around 600 BC who is still remembered for her poems about women. For his living woman he named someone called Kwan Yin, a Bodhisattva of compassion. I was wondering what a Bodhisattva is when Dr. Cobbe said, "Bruce, I was hoping for a living person who is still walking on earth among us."

Bruce said, "She is among us."

Dr. Cobbe said "Someone in a physical body, please." She said we will talk about women with religious and spiritual connections next week.

Bruce rolled his eyes and named Simone de Beauvoir, a French writer and philosopher whose book *The Second Sex* analyzes women's oppression. Then he blinked and said he wanted to name Mother Teresa, who is a nun, instead of Simone de Beauvoir. Mother Teresa runs a hospice in India for people in the untouchable caste.

That took care of the guys, but it left me wondering about Kwan Yin and if a Bodhisattva is like Aunt Stasia's Buddha.

The next woman named Amelia Earhart, the first woman to fly across the Atlantic Ocean, and Margaret Mead, an anthropologist and a Barnard alumna, who studies Samoan culture and whose work is making us rethink how we look at adolescence. She admires Margaret Mead for not being afraid to go native which fits with the way the Miss Mismatched was dressed.

The last student named Marie Curie who won two Nobel Prizes for her discovery of radium and of radioactivity. Miss Nerdy glowed as she talked about Marie Curie. For her living woman she named Cecilia Payne-Gaposchkin, an astronomer and the first person to earn a PhD in astronomy from Radcliffe College, which is connected to Harvard like Barnard and Columbia.

Payne-Gaposchkin discovered the composition of the sun is primarily hydrogen and demonstrated how that differs from the composition of the earth. All of that should have made her famous, but her male colleagues took credit for her discovery. Imagine! I would have been too outraged to spit. But Miss Nerdy said even though Gaposchkin was angry, she kept working at her research and five years ago she became the first woman full professor in Harvard's School of Arts and Sciences.

After Miss Nerdy finished talking, someone said, "Dr. Cobbe, you need to name two women as well." She laughed, but named Jane Addams and Natalie Barney.
Jane Addams brought the settlement house movement to the United States, founded Hull House, worked for peace and was awarded the Nobel Peace Prize for her work. Natalie Barney is an American poet and novelist living in Paris, France. She holds a salon in her home, a women's academy that brings together writers and artist from around the world and promotes writing by women.

Dr. Cobbe says Natalie Barney is a woman for all women, and had a great quote from her, "
At first, when an idea, a poem or the desire to write takes hold of you, work is a pleasure, a delight and your enthusiasm knows no bounds. But later on you work with difficulty, doggedly, desperately. For once you have committed yourself to a particular work, inspiration changes its form and becomes an obsession . . . which haunts you night and day. Once at grips with a work, we must master it completely before we can recover our idleness."

Then Dr. Cobbe said, "Young Scholars, so to it shall be with you. This semester, together we will study women who have mothered our history. Commit yourself to them, find your inspiration in them, become obsessed with them, master the lessons their lives hold." With that she ended the class.
What a first day of class. It was better than I ever hoped it might be. My head is still swimming with women's names, with women whose lives mattered, women who changed the world, women who are still changing the world.

I am going to enjoy Dr. Cobbe as a teacher, she is so smart. But she has this smell on her. Pungent. Not BO, not cigarette smoke, more like ammonia. I think I will enjoy her at a distance.

My philosophy class with Dr. Fredrick started too. The first day he asked each of us to say why we were taking the course. I said "to learn about the meaning of life." Dr. Fredrick rambled on and on about the meaning of the word meaning—like what language intends, what an individual is trying to show, or the significance of something. Then he went off about 'life' and how it can refer to life in general, like of a community or culture, or about a particular individual's life. He said I need to be clearer about what I mean when I say meaning of life.

Ugh.

Dr. Fredrick is as tedious as his navy blue blazer and grey serge trousers. Smyth might have been right. Maybe taking this course was a mistake. Even with all my worrying, even with all the roadblocks Dr. Smyth keeps putting in my path, I am making progress on my thesis. Mama signed the Barnard Consent Form, and I wrote to Mrs. Roosevelt asking for her permission.

Yanina, I hope she says yes. I am worried that she won't sign the forms. I used to be sure of myself. But things this summer have thrown me off my stride.

Always,

Joan

Joan to Yanina

September 15, 1961

Dear Yanina,

Remember when I asked Aunt Stasia how the letters between Mama and Mrs. Roosevelt got started and she said we would talk later? Well, yesterday I got a package from her, and she tucked in two letters that Mama wrote to her when Aunt Stasia was still working in New York City as a nurse.

Sometimes I forget that Mama and Aunt Stasia were best friends before they became sisters-in-law. But Mama first met Papa because he was Aunt Stasia's brother. I wonder what life would have been like if Papa had not died in the war. I wish I could have known Papa. I wish I could have known someone who was happy to be a free spirit. It's a good thing Mama and Aunt Stasia are savers. Now we get to see how the letters between Mama and Mrs. Roosevelt started.

When I read the letters, see an example of Fannie's coldness didn't surprise me. But Sara siding with Fannie! She is always so nice.

I can see Mama walking home from that sewing circle meeting with her back straight, not letting them see her cry when they would not let her sign the letter they all wrote together, and then writing her own letter. Mama is a woman who does what needs to be done. She doesn't show a lot of emotion. I guess I get that from her. She just does what needs to be done. I hope I get that from her too.

Anyway, I'm sending you a copy of those letters. Wait till you read them!

Always,

Joan

Eva Zatańczy, Jersey Homesteads, New Jersey to Anastasia Zatańczy, New York, New York

January 26, 1940

Dearest Stasia,

My life is a salad! Just when I get all the pieces nicely layered up and looking pretty, someone takes a bite out of it and everything goes all Henny Penny helter skeltering.
Our little town keeps struggling to preserve the factory. But the possibility of the factory closing is all that the sewing circle ladies talk about.

The other day Brony came home from work at the farm all excited. He had been changing the newspapers they use for the chickens' bedding and saw an old "My Day" Column by Mrs. Eleanor Roosevelt from last July. It was about her trip to visit Arthurdale, West Virginia, a Subsistence Homestead town like us. Mrs. Roosevelt wrote about the people there, their projects and her concern for the town. Brony thought if I showed it to our sewing circle, we could write to Mrs. Roosevelt and she might help our town too.

All of us in the sewing circle talked over the idea. We talked about whether it was a good idea, and then we talked about what we wanted to tell Mrs. Roosevelt about our situation. I took notes, went home and worked it into a letter. The next day we all read it over, changed it some, made it sound a little more formal. After we finished going over the letter, we read it aloud to hear how it sounded and made a few more changes.

When it was just right, I typed it up all neat and clean. We passed the clean copy around the table. Our emotions were a hodgepodge of anxiety, pride, and hope as each woman signed it. Fannie was sitting next to me. She signed. I reached over to add my name. She held onto the letter and said, "I think only women from the original families who invested in the cooperatives should sign the letter. We have suffered the most. We stand to lose the most."

Stasia, I tell you, I was shocked to my soul. We all sat together writing that letter. But Fannie was saying she did not want my name on it. I looked around the table. The other ladies looked down at their coffee cups. Then Sara said, "I'm sorry Eva, but Fannie has a point. We don't blame you for renting here. But, the letter should come from the original cooperative members." Sara said the original members were the ones who put their life savings into the cooperatives and into building the town.

The ladies said that they were glad that Brony and I were living in Jersey Homesteads now, and that we are good neighbors. But if things fall apart here, we can move on to somewhere else. For the original cooperative members, they can't just pick up and leave. They have invested all they have in the town and the cooperatives.

My gut twisted into a double half hitch knot. Tears burned my eyes, but I would not let them see me cry. Brony and I joined the store and the farm cooperatives as soon as we got here. We filled out the forms and got all the approvals. Even after that, they only approved us as auxiliary members, because we did not contribute funds to the founding of the cooperatives. We are not original homesteaders, we are only renters. But we joined anyway. Brony and I try to do everything we can to fit in as members of the community.

We work hard to fit in. Brony noticed that on Thursday nights people are out sweeping their sidewalks and the road in front of their house. So every Thursday we are out there right along with everyone else sweeping our sidewalks and the road. Brony always makes sure we sweep the road a good bit past our property on either side of us. We do everything we can to be respectful and respectable. We made it a point to take a walk around town most nights, to smile and say 'hello' to people we passed on our walks.

If folks are sitting in their yards, we stop and pass some time chatting with them. We both believe these little things will open a place for us in town. We both work at it, trying our best to be good neighbors.

Mr. Stein, next door, must have notice us sweeping with everyone else, because one night when we were walking he called Brony over and told him, "We always sweep north to south and west to east, the way the waters flow to the ocean. Homestead Lane is an east-west road, we always start our sweeping on the west side of the property. None of this hit or miss some weeks start on one side, some weeks start on the other side."

And with that he gave me a smile and a wave, nodded to Brony, and walked into his house. Now every Thursday, we begin our sweeping on the Stein's side of our property, the west side, and we sweep to the east where Fannie and her family live. We gather up every bit of debris from the street so that Fannie has nothing to clean up from us. We are careful so there can be no complaints about the renters. We are as much a part of town as we can be. We are associate members of the cooperatives, but we are only associate members, not original members.

Anyway, back at the sewing circle, they all agreed that my name should not go on the letter. I understood then, that even though they act all nice to me at our sewing circle gatherings, I am still not one of them. I gathered my things and walked home with my heart in my shoes. When I got home, I sat myself down and cried my eyes out, long onion tears. Then I got up, made myself a cup of tea (the idea of coffee turned my stomach sour). I thought, if I can't sign their letter, then I will write my own letter to Mrs. Roosevelt. And that is what I did. I got out my best pen and paper, and in my neatest hand writing, I wrote my letter to Mrs. Roosevelt.

Stasia, I have gone and written to Mrs. Eleanor Roosevelt, the wife of the President of the United States of America. Why I might as well write a letter to that movie star, Ginger Rogers!

I mailed the letter yesterday. Do you think anything will come of it? Stasia, do you think I am crazy?

After I mailed the letter, when Brony got home from work at the farm, I told him what I had done. He looked at me with a new look in his eyes, a different, I don't know, respect? Then he gave me one of his big old bear hugs, and whispered in my ear, "I didn't know I married a trouble maker. Let's make trouble some together."

Oh, your brother! What have I done!

Your loving sister-in-law in trouble,

Eva

Eva Zatańczy, Jersey Homesteads, New Jersey to Anastasia Zatańczy, New York, New York

February 29, 1940

Dearest Stasia,

You will never believe what was in our mail when I picked it up at the post office today. There was a letter for me with the United States White House return address! Can you believe it? I'm not sure I believe it myself.

Stasia, after I sent off that letter to Mrs. Roosevelt, days passed and nothing happened. Days turned into weeks, still nothing. Truth be told, I put the letter out of my mind and tried to forget about it. I told myself nothing would come of it. I was sad, because I had hoped, but even when I was writing it I knew the chances were the letter would not find its way to Mrs. Roosevelt.

When I was picking up the mail at the post office today, I saw the return address, and was beside myself. Then I decided it was one of those form letters government officials send when you write to them. A letter that says "Thank you for your concern. I am always pleased to hear from my constituents. I will take your thoughts into consideration."

When I got home, I sat there and stared at the letter, imagining it might actually be from Mrs. Roosevelt. I wanted to share it with someone. But Brony was at work on the farm, and you were in New York at work in the hospital. I went around in circles in my mind, then I hugged that letter to my chest, gathered up my courage, set aside my hopes and expectations, and set out to find a letter opener.

I would not rip open a letter from the White House all willy-nilly. Oh no. It might be a form letter, but it was from the White House. It needed to be opened neatly and properly. I opened every drawer in the kitchen. I looked under the napkins and table clothes. I looked behind the plates and glasses. I emptied our junk drawer, cleaned it, threw out what we don't use and then put the rest back all clean and neatly organized. I got so involved with cleaning the drawer, I almost forgot about the letter opener. Finally, I opened the side drawer in the desk in the spare room, and there was the letter opener large as life, waiting for me to find it.

I wondered, "Why is whatever you are looking for always in the last place that you look?" I thought for a minute. Then I laughed, because what kind of fool would continue to look for something after they found it. It must be in the last place you look, because after you find it, you stop looking.

I took the letter opener, sat down at the kitchen table, and ever so carefully, slit the letter open. Stasia, it was an actual letter from Mrs. Eleanor Roosevelt, wife of the president, the First Lady of the United States of America. Addressed to me. Signed by her personally. It contained an invitation for me to write to her. Now that is something! The Wife of the President of the United States invited me to be her pen pal!

Of course I will write to her.

Then I worried myself into a tizzy. How soon should I write to her? I do not want to pester her with too many letters. But I don't want her to think I didn't appreciate her interest, or that I did not want to correspond with her, or that I did not appreciate what she has done for us. But I don't want to be a pest.

What should I write about? Certainly I will tell her what happens with the factory and Kartiganer and Company. But, should I tell her about Brony and me? The sewing circle ladies? Stories that might bring a little lightness to her days? She must get awfully tied down with serious tasks and responsibilities. Maybe some of the brightness of our days here in Jersey Homesteads might carry some lightness to the intensity of her life.

Of course I made a plan, because I am nothing if not a planner. Once a month on the third Tuesday of the month, after the bills are paid, the laundry and the cleaning done, I will set myself down and write a letter to my new pen pal, Mrs. Eleanor Roosevelt. That is what I will do.

Stasia, you must tell me all the news with you. How is your new friend Barbara? Or is it Babs? I forget now. Do tell me all the adventures are you having in that city of wonders.

Your loving sister-in-law,

Eva

Joan to Yanina

September 19, 1961

Dear Yanina,

So much is happening. I have to tell you or I will explode! And I need to stay busy or I think about being pregnant and I worry myself crazy. It helps when I write to you; it keeps me from worrying.

First, Mama forbids me to even think about dropping out of college. She says that if I really want to keep the baby, she and Aunt Stasia will take care of her while I'm in school (I just know she is a girl), but I have to finish college. I am definitely going to keep her now that I can see how having a baby gives meaning to my life.

One day last week I was sitting on the library steps thinking, pondering my life and staring into space. Dr. Cobbe was walking towards the library, saw me, sat down by my side and said, "Earth to Joan. Care to share?" Yanina, I don't know what came over me. Something about Dr. Cobbe reminds me of a lady leprechaun, the way she talks with a lilt, the way her eyes twinkle. But her clothes have a pretty pungent aroma when you get close to her. And she always wears pants suits. Never a skirt or dress. Always pants suits, and always with a band of cat fur around the bottom of her pants legs. But she is really nice.

I poured my heart out to her, about Harold getting me pregnant and how I don't know how I will manage the expense of the baby, about how Harold said I was on my own if I kept the baby, about how he should have to take responsibility for the baby. But don't know how I can hold him accountable.

Yanina, smoke came out of Dr. Cobbe's ears when I told her about Smyth. She got so angry at what he did to me, the lady leprechaun turned into a fire-breathing dragon! She said Harold can't just walk away from me. I can take him to court and the judge will make him pay child support. The campus branch of Legal Aid at Columbia works on a pro bono basis for Columbia and Barnard students and they will help me file a paternity suit.

I am considering it. But if I know Smyth, he will find a way out of it. But, I've got nothing to lose by trying.
All of that keeps circling around in my head like a swarm of bees. So let me tell you about Women in History (which is amazing!)—if only to distract myself.

After I wrote to you last week, I noticed how I had the names of the women each student mentioned, but not of the students. Lucky for me, this week Dr. Cobbe started class by calling the roll, so I got everyone's name. Tee-shirt woman is Patricia. The older woman is KarenMarie, who keeps looking at me with this look, like a question, in her eyes. Miss coed is Sandy. Beatnik Girl with the purple headband is Pamela. Mousey girl is Rebecca. Miss Mismatched clothes is Rita. The nerdy woman is Sylvia.

My head was aching from concentrating so hard to get all those names straight, and class hadn't even started. I am so bad with remembering names. In Roosevelt, everyone already knows everyone else, I never learned how to remember the names of new people.

The guys' names were easier because there are only four of them. Kevin sits next to Rebecca and they have the same last name, so they must be related. I remembered that the invisible man with the tan is Bruce. Mr. Preppy of Brooks Brothers is Gregory, and he wants to be called 'Gregory' not Greg. The artsy looking guy is Curtis. The guys all spend way too much time checking out us girls. As if we even cared about guys in a course on women in history.

Dr. Cobbe was intense this week. Right after roll call she got down to business. We have our first paper due in six weeks and we have to go on a field trip for the paper. We have to attend a women's event: a lecture on a women's issue, a concert by a women's group, a consciousness-raising group, a meeting of a group working to make things better for women, anything as long as the event is about women in some way or another. She isn't giving us names of specific events or groups, we have to figure that out on our own. We have to team up, choose, and attend the event with our group. But each of us has to write a reaction paper describing the event we attended, what happened, our personal reaction to the event, and an analysis of how it relates to the course.

When Dr. Cobbe said it was time to choose our groups, Gregory said "but we barely know each other. How can we decide who we want to be in a group with?"

Dr. Cobbe half smiled and said, "It's a partner for one project, not a lifetime commitment. You will each write your own paper, let me be clear on that. You will attend the event together, and each group will briefly describe the event they attended to the rest of the class. But writing the paper is an independent, individual project.

"Still, I take your point. Let's go around the circle again, once more with feeling. Please repeat your name and name a woman you respect who is a leading figure in religion or spirituality. Say a word or two describing the woman's importance to you." Dr. Cobbe started with Bruce because he already had a claim on Kwan Yin.

Bruce looked elated. He's cute when he gets all enthusiastic. He thought for a second, laughed, said he just came from a class about haiku and proclaimed, "Bodhisattva Kwan Yin; enlightened being; kind-hearted compassion." After he finished, Bruce looked like a satisfied Buddha himself.

Rita named Aphrodite, looked at Bruce, winked and said: Greek Aphrodite; goddess of love and beauty; regal splendor and radiance. A few of the guys mumbled "Whoa baby." Dr. Cobbe gave them her look, not quite a stink eye, just short of the evil eye. A couple of the women looked at Rita and said, "Nice." Rita sat up an inch taller.

Sylvia said: Hindu Sarasvati; knowledge, arts, wisdom and learning; grace with persistence and focus.

It was my turn next. I was distracted taking notes on what the others were saying, and I wasn't sure who I wanted to name, but then I remembered, "If I perish, I perish," and how Zayde would tell us about Esther saving the Jewish people from being slaughtered, because she begged the King for their lives, and she did it at a time when if you spoke to the King without his invitation, it could mean instant death. But the King didn't kill her, he listened to her. I said: Facing her peril; challenging her King; Esther saved her people.

Yanina, remembering Esther reminded me that even when things look hopeless, if you keep thinking and act with your head and your heart, you can create options.
Patricia claimed the Amazons, fierce women warriors, fighting for right and justice.

KarenMarie said: Yemaya African Mother; goddess of moon, water and childbirth; conceiver of courage and strength.

Miss coed, Sandy claimed Mary the Mother of Jesus Christ, Queen of Heaven, reigning over mere men on earth. She wiggled her eyebrows and said that men don't control heaven even if they do control the Catholic Church. That got a laugh from everyone.

Pamela named Pandora, bringer of gifts; goddess of art, crafts, weaving and agriculture. Curtis said something about opening Pandora's Box. She stared him down and said, "That's nothin' but a patriarchal myth. Men got jealous of the respect and reverence Pandora received, so they created those lies about her."
This course is going to be giving me a lot to think about.

Rebecca named Grandmother Spider Woman, weaver of the universe, Cherokee goddess of wisdom and creation. She imagines Grandmother Spider Woman behind the scenes, pulling all the strings. That is neither unobtrusive nor mousey.
Kevin named Danu, Irish goddess of knowledge, source of all life, friend to the fairies. His grandparents came to the United States from Ireland and taught him Celtic mythology.

Gregory said: Freyja, Scandinavian fertility goddess, spirit of family abundance. His people came to the United States from Norway. He wants to have a large family, and he is counting on Freyja to help. Kevin mumbled that Gregory should count on a breathing girl not a goddess. Gregory said he was counting on both.

Finally we got to Curtis, who is not a man of few words. He named the Muses, a collection of Greek goddesses who inspire artists. Today we acknowledge nine Muses, but originally there were only three. *Melete* of water and practice. *Mneme* of sound, air and memory. *Aoide* of voice and song. Curtis reveres the Muses because he is going to be a novelist.

Then we all looked at Dr. Cobbe. Somehow as we named our women, it was a normal class thing. But for Dr. Cobbe to name a goddess in her life seemed kind of too intimate. But, she when ahead and said: Baba Yaga, wild Russian witch; mistress of magic and wisdom; fearless mother of power and self-knowledge. Dr. Cobbe's eyes twinkled as she said she liked Baba Yaga because that's how she wants to be when she grows up. Like she isn't already a grown up.

But Dr. Cobbe got an energy around her when she was talking about Baba Yaga. She was a kid again. It was there and then not, but there was a flash of something. (And yes, I know no one managed an actual haiku, but what you do in a small town when you can't dance? We mangled and tangled and giggled our way through.)

Dr. Cobbe stood up, and asked the women to partner with each other. She asked us to mill around, and then stand next to the woman we wanted to partner with. Before I could blink, Pamela was standing next to me asking me to partner with her. I wanted to partner with KarenMarie to find out why she keeps looking at me, and Pamela gives me the willies, but I liked how Pamela named Pandora, and she was standing right there, so I agreed.

When the women were partnered, Dr. Cobbe told us to invite one of the guys to join us. Pamela and I looked at each other, and both said Bruce. We stepped over to where he was sitting and formed our trinity.

Next Dr. Cobbe asked the small groups to discuss the women each of us had named, to find commonalities and differences among them.

Pamela, Bruce and I introduced ourselves to each other. Bruce is Bruce Sharma, which means joy, comfort and happiness. Pamela is Pamela Frost, and she hates being called Pam. I said I am Joan Zatańczy, which means to dance in Polish, and that I am from Roosevelt, NJ. Bruce's eyes twinkled and he called me Joan of Roosevelt. (He was the guy who winked at me last week. What's with that?) Then we talked about things that are important for the women we named: courage, strength, independence. I wondered if any of our women ever struggled to find themselves. Pamela wondered if any of them ever thought they were lost.

Dr. Cobbe called all the groups together, we reported on our discussions, and she said our next step is to choose an event to attend. She also said that some women's events might be women only, so we should call the organizers of the event we are planning to attend. If they say the event is women only, we should thank them and try somewhere else. That's fine by me. If they don't want us, I don't want to be there.

Yanina, as I'm writing to you, I've got myself thinking about what I said about Esther (how if you remember to keep thinking and acting with both your head and your heart, there are options) and about Patricia's Amazons fighting for what is right and just. When I think about Esther and the Amazons and all of those other powerful women, I can feel my anger with Harold flowing up my backbone like a volcano, I can taste my power.

Suddenly I've got all these emotions flaring up all over the place. So much for being the queen of reason. I guess I really am pregnant!

When I finish this letter to you, I am going to make an appointment to see those Legal Aid people and ask them to help me file a paternity suit against Harold.

Always,

Joan

Joan to Yanina

September 24, 1961

Dear Yanina,

Pamela, Bruce and I met up at Jake. Have I told you that the first floor of Barnard Hall is called 'Jake.' The plaque on the floor honors Jake Schiff who donated Barnard Hall to the college. (But really, is it an honor to have people walking on his name all the time? And why we don't call it Schiff?) Anyway, Jake is the student center, where all the important posters are, where everyone hangs out. Jake is where to go if you are not in class or the library.

So, we went to Jake, got our coffee (cold and bitter, but cheap) found a table, and sat there looking at each other. It was like being on a first date with two people. As much as we talked in class, now we had nothing to say. After we sat there looking at each other for half of forever, Pamela mumbled that she'd like to go to a Daughters of Bilitis meeting but she didn't know how Bruce would feel about it, or how they would feel about a guy being there.

Bruce looked at the table and said, "I don't know if I should . . . but . . . well. I have two older sisters. And my oldest sister, I'm not sure. I mean I guess I should talk to her, but I don't want to piss her off."

Pamela looked at Bruce and said, "What?"

Bruce swallowed and said, "Well, I think my oldest sister, Rhoda, is a lesbian, but I'm not sure. I don't want to ask her because if I'm wrong she would kill me. If she is, I want to be supportive. So, if we could go to that group, if they wouldn't mind me being there because I'm a guy, I could find out some stuff about lesbians and all."

Pamela looked relieved, which was interesting. She got all hip and said, "Most cool. Mr. Bruce."

Pamela said a branch of the Daughters of Bilitis meets in the Greenwich Village and she knows somebody, who knows someone, who knows where and when they meet. I don't know why the thought of going to a lesbian group creeps me out, but it does. But, since I didn't have any other ideas, and since both Pamela and Bruce want to go, I agreed. What I didn't say was that I was wondering how Pamela knew about the group and why it's important to her. Stay tuned Yanina, I am getting ready to meet my first lesbians. How weird is that?

And, that's the news from Barnard College.

But I have to tell you one more thing. In yesterday's "My Day" Column, Mrs. Roosevelt mentioned this new program President Kennedy is starting. It's called the Peace Corps and they send volunteers to other countries to help them with projects like building schools or wells and other stuff. If I weren't having a baby, I would sign up when I graduate. I am beginning to see how having a baby will complicate things.

I'm starting to worry about whether Mrs. Roosevelt got my letter. I hope she will sign the Barnard forms. I can't imagine what I would do if she won't give her consent for me to use her letters to Mama for my senior thesis.

Anyway, way at the bottom of the sack of letters, I found the first letter that Mrs. Roosevelt wrote to Mama. Mrs. Roosevelt did ask Mama to keep writing to her. I'm sending that letter to you.

What's your tale, Nightingale? What's new in Kasefet?

Always,

Joan

The First Letter from Mrs. Eleanor Roosevelt to Eva Zatańczy
Mrs. Franklin D. Roosevelt

1600 Pennsylvania Avenue
Washington, DC
February 12, 1940

Mrs. Bronislaw Zatańczy
224 Homesteads Lane
Jersey Homesteads, New Jersey

Dear Mrs. Zatańczy,

I have received your letter describing the circumstances of the good families in Jersey Homesteads. I am sorry to hear your family has encountered such difficult circumstances upon moving into a town that held such high hopes for you. I commend your resolve and resilience in getting to know your neighbors and becoming friendly with them. My experience has been that it is much harder to be difficult with people you know and understand. I trust your effort will further the understanding and good will between you and your neighbors.

I have made the Farm Securities Administration's Mr. Rexford Tugwell aware of my concern for the people of Jersey Homesteads, and my interest in seeing the negotiations with Kartiganer and Company of New York City proceed as expeditiously as possible. With the Nazi's creating turmoil in Europe and with the Soviet Union's attack on Finland yesterday, domestic matters have been overshadowed by the enormity of world events.

However, you may trust that I will advocate strongly on your behalf.

As you may know I enjoy a continuing friendship with the Homestead Project in Arthurdale, West Virginia. Those settlers are also struggling to find their way in building the community of their expectations. Now I am pleased to have an opportunity to develop a friendship with Jersey Homesteads. The Homestead Projects have been an important element in Franklin's plans to help lift the people of our country from the depths of this economic depression. I look forward with great interest to hearing of your progress in Jersey Homesteads. Please do keep me informed.

Sincerely yours,

Mrs. Eleanor Roosevelt

Eleanor Roosevelt to Joan Zatańczy

October 2, 1961

Dear Joan,

I was pleased to receive your letter updating me on your collegiate progress. Over the years, your mother and I have grown close to each other through our epistolary exchanges. And I am delighted that our letters have inspired you to study the contributions of women to our culture and country.

Many women have played important roles in my education and growth. Women have mattered deeply, and for the better, in my life. I suspect—no, I know—women have mattered deeply, and for the better, in our world. But far too often the knowledge of that difference has been erased. How wonderful that you are taking a course on Women in History. I hope it will provide you with rich opportunities to examine the contributions of an expansive array of women across countries, cultures and generations.

Joan, I understand you want to focus your senior thesis on my work with the United Nations and the *Universal Declaration of Human Rights*. But, I think time has yet to tell what impact that document will have. History has yet to be lived, let alone written on that work.

There are so many other women who have done important things. Perhaps you should study their contributions rather than my work at the United Nations?

As I write this letter to you, I am remembering a small dinner party at the Saugatuck, Connecticut home of Miss Lillian Wald in early August 1933, during Franklin's first term as president. Elinor Morgenthau and I were driving from Hyde Park to Washington DC, and we decided to stop and pay Lillian a visit on our way. There were six of us seated at the dinner table that evening.

Let me introduce those women to you, Joan.

Seated to my right was Elinor Morgenthau, my traveling companion. Elinor was married to Henry Morgenthau, Franklin's Treasury Secretary. But to me, Elinor was a dear friend. I relied on her keen intellect and clarity of insight. Dear Elinor passed away a few years after the dinner party, in 1945 when she was only 54. I have missed her every day since then. But that evening in 1933, Elinor was in fine form and it was a joy to be seated by her side.

To Elinor's right was Lillian Wald, whose home we were visiting. Because Lillian was recovering from surgery, many of her friends were calling on her to help in whatever ways we could and to be sure she was taking proper care of herself. We would lose Lillian seven years later, when she was 73.

As I reflect on Lillian's life, I suspect that surgery was the beginning of her decline. A nurse by profession, Lillian founded the Henry Street Settlement House in New York City. She led Henry Street for forty years and developed medical, social service and cultural programs for the residents of that area. Lillian was a valiant leader for social reform, public health, world peace and human rights. She helped to found visiting nurses, Women's Trade Union League, and Women's International League for Peace and Freedom (WILPF).

To the right of Lillian sat Dr. Alice Hamilton. Alice and Lillian had known each other since 1915 when they worked together with a wonderful cadre of women to bring peace to our world during a World War. Alice is a physician who worked with Jane Addams at Hull House in Chicago. She is quite the expert in occupational health. She created the field of toxicology through her study of occupational illnesses and the effects of industrial metals and chemical compounds on the human body. She was the first woman appointed to the faculty at Harvard Medical School.

Now at the ripe old age of 92, our dear Alice is still with us. Perhaps you might interview her for your senior thesis?

To Alice's right sat Jane Addams. Jane helped to bring the Settlement House movement to the United States from London, and she founded Hull House in Chicago. Joan, how I wish you could have met Jane Addams, but we lost her two years after the dinner. She was a powerhouse. Once she put her mind to something, it would happen.

At its zenith, Hull House was home to more than twenty of the brightest and most innovative women this country has ever known. When we had our dinner in 1933, we were still celebrating Jane's receipt of the Nobel Peace Prize in 1931.

To Jane's right and my left sat Margaret Sanger. Margaret and I disagree on many things, but she is a staunch advocate for women's right to knowledge, techniques and tools to understand and control the reproductive process. Margaret and her friends coined the term 'birth control.' They argued that women would never stand on an equal footing with men until they had control over their reproductive functions. When we met for our dinner, Margaret was actively campaigning for the change of laws that denied women access to the means of birth control. Margaret must be nearly 82 now. She is still with us and still working to advance women's control over their reproductive functions. She would be an interesting candidate to interview for your thesis.

If you decide to interview either Alice or Margaret for your research, I will provide you with a letter of introduction.
When we gathered that night at Lillian's home, Elinor and I were the youngest of the group, she was 42 and I was 49. Margaret was 54, Lillian and Alice were both nearly 66. Jane claimed the role of elder mother at 73.

Oh, Joan, what stories were told that night. What dreams were shared, and what fears were spoken. Alice had just published an article on Adolph Hitler and the youth in Germany, and she was gravely concerned regarding the threat of war Hitler's activities posed. Those concerns got Lillian, Alice and Jane reflecting on their work for peace during World War I. Jane recounted a terrible time in her life when she had returned from Europe where she visited some of our boys at the front lines. In a speech she gave at Carnegie Hall in New York City, Jane described how in anticipation of an order to put bayonets on their rifles and charge, the boys took a drink of brandy to stiffen their nerves. Jane wanted to show the people in the audience how terrifying battles are. But the newspapers got hold of the bit of the story regarding the brandy, and they accused her of calling our boys drunks and cowards. That is not what Jane meant, but for weeks and months afterwards people would throw rotten vegetables and fruit at her. Jane said she could manage for herself, but the donations and funding to her projects at Hull House dried up precipitously, and she had a much more difficult time finding ways to keep them afloat.

When she heard Jane's story, Margaret sighed deeply, offered Jane her sympathies, and said, "But at least they didn't try to kill your sister." Margaret described a moment in 1916 when a group including Margaret and her sister Ethel were arrested for creating a public nuisance when they protested the closing of one of their clinics for women.

Ethel's trial was first, she was convicted, and sentenced to thirty days of hard labor. Four days into her sentence, she went on a hunger strike. The judge would have none of that and ordered her force fed. She resisted, and would have died at their hands if they had not been able to get her pardoned.
Joan, one lesson we all took from that evening's stories was that even though we were doing important work, often we did not realize the ways in which we were putting our lives on the line when we took up that work. As Margaret reminded us all, idealism is wonderful, but it doesn't pay the bills, it doesn't keep the dogs away. It is vital that we all hold close to each other, and support and protect each other's well-being and dreams.

I am convinced Margaret was correct in her analysis. Women need to hold together if we will keep our ideals high, our dreams alive and our bodies and spirits in good health. Joan, the day you stop dreaming is the day you become old. But it is important to remember that many of the women who have worked for peace and for women's rights have been arrested, threatened, and isolated by their friends and family. Many of these exemplary women have experienced serious physical harm. Those are high costs to pay. We need to be able to rely on each other if we hope to survive those costs.

Later in the evening as we gazed at the embers in the fireplace, Jane recalled her meeting with Leo Tolstoy in Russia. Jane always loved to tell a story. Tolstoy had long been one of her heroes. She was enamored with his activism and writing. To hear her tell it, she had read and reread everything he ever wrote.

In 1896, seven years after she founded Hull House, as she was recovering from typhoid, Jane took a vacation to Europe with Mary Rozet Smith her lifelong friend and companion. While they were in Europe, they visited Tolstoy. He came in from working the fields, wiped his hands in a towel, took one look at the two of them who wore long dresses with billowing sleeves as was the style, and boomed, "Madame I was told you are a reformer who worked with the poor, but the fabric on one arm of your dress would generously provide an entire frock for a girl."

Jane was taken aback, but stood her ground. As they talked, Jane mentioned that part of the funding for Hull House came from her family estate which included a working farm. Tolstoy bellowed at her again for being an absentee landlord and asked her how she thought she was helping the people by adding herself to the crowded city rather than by tilling her own soil.

Jane said the encounter distressed her. She and Mary left Tolstoy's residence and continued their trip with the luster of her hero tarnished and with Jane doubting her confidence and questioning her approach to working at Hull House. Upon her return to Chicago she began working in the Hull House bakery. But, by the time her hours at the bakery were done, there were lines of people waiting to see her, piles of letters to be answered, and human needs and wants waiting.

She decided that saving her soul by baking bread did not justify setting aside the needs of real human beings. From her encounter with Tolstoy she strengthened her belief in the value of compassion and caring leadership. She also strengthened her trust in the words and wisdom of good women with open minds and hearts.

Now, Joan, let me ask you, "Was Jane Addams extravagant in her dress? Was Tolstoy self-indulgent in his labor?" They were both convinced of their correctness, and they both carried streaks of stubborn intransigence. Leaders need to embody confidence, but good leaders also need to learn to temper their stubbornness if they mean to nurture future leaders and to sustain dynamic creativity within their cause.

That evening we were all feeling the strains and pulls of our past struggles, so we particularly enjoyed each other's company and comradery. I believe it was the endearing spell of Lillian's personality and the power of her sympathetic understanding that enabled us to weave our stories together that night.

How I learned from the stories those women told during that dinner party. As I listened to Lillian, I notice how she always saw people as individuals, never as congregate humanity, and therein, I believe, is the secret to her ability to relate to human suffering with her endless and undying compassion.

In Jane's stories I heard her commitment to teaching through her actions and example; to creating a life built on cooperation and affirming the potential of others; and to deep and inclusive democratic relationships. These women leaders lived their highest ideals.

When they dared to dream, the reality of those dreams danced ever closer along the horizon of our world. It was a heady night, that dinner with those women. Even now all these years later I can see their faces, their voices resonate in my heart.

How I wish for you, dear young Joan, a circle of friends and mentors such as those women have been to me. I wish for you a productive semester filled with the joy that comes from good learning and warm love.

Joan, you see there is an abundance of options available to you for your study. There are many powerful women whose work you might select.

But, if you are still set on my work with the United Nations as your project, well, then follow your heart. You will find primary source material and the answers to your questions in my "My Day" Columns. You may want to look for columns on Arthurdale, West Virginia and Mrs. Bertha Brodsky.

I know they are available in Franklyn's library at Hyde Park. I expect archives of "My Day" are housed in many libraries, but I know the collection at Hyde Park is complete.

I have include a signed copy of your College's Consent Form with this letter and I have included an affirmation of my longstanding correspondence with your mother, which should put to rest questions related to the provenance of the letters.

I am also including a letter of introduction for you to take to the librarians at Hyde Park. Franklyn's library is open to the public, and the librarians there are gracious, but perhaps an extra introduction will be of help to you. I wish you interesting explorations as you move forward with your research.

Fondly,

Mrs. Roosevelt

Joan to Mrs. Roosevelt

October 9, 1961

Dear Mrs. Roosevelt,

Thank you for your letter. Thank you so very much for signing the Barnard forms, and for suggesting your "My Day" Column as an additional primary source.

Reading about the dinner party at Miss Wald's home was a revelation. The women you described were both strong and powerful, and human and vulnerable. Your stories about them helped me to see them as actual people, not as heroes on a pedestal.

I really appreciate your signing the Barnard forms because even after reading about all of those other women, I still want to do my senior thesis on your work at the United Nations. Every time I reread the *Universal Declaration of Human Rights*, I am astonished that my Mama knows the woman behind its creation. I appreciate your suggesting those other women in your letter, but I still have my heart set on studying your work.

I can't wait to get to the library at Hyde Park to explore the "My Day" Columns you wrote during your tenure at the United Nations. I read your column every day in the newspaper now and I appreciate the wisdom and inspiration you share.

My friend Pamela and I will take the train up to the library as soon as we get through our quarterly exams this semester. Pamela is doing her senior thesis on President Roosevelt's Homestead Subsistence Division.

Thank you so much for all of your help. Mama and Aunt Stasia said to tell you they send you their best.

Sincerely,

Joan Zatańczy

Joan to Yanina

October 9, 1961

Dear Yanina,

I know this is illogical, but while I want to have this baby and I am sure that loving this baby will be the grand meaning of my life, I am also furious that I am pregnant and I am furious that Harold got me pregnant and thinks he can get away with it.

After I wrote to you last month, I marched myself over to the Legal Aid office on Columbia's campus. They are helping me file a paternity suit against Harold. He should have gotten the court papers by now, but I haven't heard anything from him. What is he waiting for?

Last weekend I was home in Roosevelt and decided that I had better tell Bubba and Zayde that I am pregnant. Bubba tsked, Zayde shook his head, said, "*Dziewczyna*, my girl." They each said that they love me, and they will love my baby. Zayde gave me one of his bear hugs. Bubba tsked some more. That was it. Classic Bubba and Zayde. No drama, just love.

Yanina, I got a letter from Mrs. Roosevelt, and she said I could use her letters for my thesis. In her letter she wrote about all these other women that I could study, but I still want to study her work at the United Nations.

And, talk about the United Nations, we all better get focused on peace, because around here everyone is going crazy about the dangers of nuclear war, Even Mrs. Roosevelt. Today, her "My Day" Column discussed planning for the effects of a nuclear war: who should be in charge of fallout shelters, how to stock them with food and water, and how to get clean air into them. Ever since the Soviet Union started testing nuclear bombs above ground, everyone is bomb shelter crazy. The Barnard Bulletin has been running articles debating whether there should be shelters on campus. I even overheard Bubba telling Mama and Aunt Stasia that she wants to build a shelter behind the house, to protect the baby—my baby—after she is born.

The United Nations is the topic of the semester at Barnard. Since Dag Hammarskjold died on September 16th, the freshman orientation lectures are honoring him and are examining the work of the United Nations. And, the Barnard Bulletin announced that the 60s Seminar will also discuss the United Nations. The timing is perfect for using Mrs. Roosevelt's work at the UN for my senior thesis.
By the way, I got a note from President Barrows. He wants to meet with me. I have to call his secretary and schedule an appointment. I wonder what that is about. It is too early to identify the class valedictorian, and I'm not graduating in May, anyway. I wonder what he wants.

Last week Pamela, Bruce and I attended the Daughter's of Bilitis meeting for our Women in History class project. We all took the subway to Greenwich Village. While we were on the subway Bruce said he thinks Dr. Cobbe is one of those feminists. Pamela asked Bruce what difference it makes, he shrugged and said, none, he was just wondering. Bruce asked if we had heard about Dr. Smyth's newest escapade. He said the gossip is Smyth got some undergrad pregnant, and he is escaping faculty vengeance by moving to Stanford University. Pamela smacked Bruce on the back of his head and said, "What's wrong with you." I sat up a little taller and said, "I'm that undergrad. And Smyth will escape nothing. I'm taking him to court for child support."

Then there was by a thundering silence among us until our stop at Union Square.

We got off the subway and walked by St. Vincent's Hospital where Aunt Stasia used to work. We walked down 7th Avenue towards Bleecker Street. Bleecker Street has the cutest little shops. But we had to get to that meeting on time, so I had to pass them all by. It was a long walk, but we found MacDougal Street and the address we were looking for. We buzzed the apartment, a woman answered, and Pamela said, "Sappho's sister sends salutations." I was nervous, it felt bizarre to use a secret password, and I giggled. Pamela didn't actually say, "grow up" but her look sure did.

The woman buzzed us in, and we walked up to the apartment where the meeting was being held. With the extra weight I'm carrying, climbing steps keeps getting harder. When we got to the third floor, it took me a minute to catch my breath, then we knocked on the door and a woman opened it and said, "Hi my name is Babs. Welcome."

We introduced ourselves. Seeing Bruce confused Babs, but then a look of recognition flashed in her eyes when we said we were from Barnard. She told us to mingle around and introduce ourselves to the women.

In we went. The living room was enormous, filled with overstuffed chairs and sofas. There were paintings, photographs and posters of women on the walls, only women. A poster of Radclyffe Hall said she wrote a book called the *Well of Loneliness*. Pamela told us the book is about lesbians in the 1880s and the book was put on trial for obscenity. (Who puts a book on trial? I have to read it, even if it is about lesbians.) Above the fireplace was a painting of a beautiful woman. Pamela told us the woman was Renée Vivien, one of Natalie Barney's lovers. (Now I am wondering about Dr. Cobbe naming Natalie Barney as a woman she admires.)

Bruce looked around the room and whispered, "Isn't this supposed to be all women? What are those guys doing over there?" Pamela gave him an elbow and said, "They are women, you fool. Haven't you ever heard of a dyke?"

Bruce said, "You mean like to prevent floods?"

Pamela rolled her eyes and said, "Like in butch and femme. And let's keep it down. We don't want to get thrown out before the meeting even starts."

A woman came over and said, "No one gets thrown out of here, kids. At least not without a good reason. You must be the three college students who called? I'm glad to see you made it. My name is Marion."

With Marion introducing us, we met most of the other fifteen or sixteen women. You cannot imagine sixteen more unique people if you tried. All sizes, all ages, some dressed up, some in work clothes, some in dresses, some in pants. And all of them lesbians, except us. But, they were all nice.
As the women found places to sit and settle in, one more woman arrived. Babs gave her a hug and asked about someone named Shelia. At that the woman started crying. She said she came to tell everyone what happened last night when Shelia was walking home from Mona's Royal Roost on Cornelia Street in Greenwich Village. A bunch of thugs beat Shelia up, and called her "lesbo, bitch, dyke and whore." They kept calling her those names and punching and kicking her in the gut and face. They even kicked out her front teeth. Shelia won't go to the hospital, because she is afraid that the hospital will call the police and the police will ask what she was doing at Mona's because everyone knows it is a lesbian bar. Shelia is afraid the police will talk to people where she works, and she might lose her job if they find out she is a lesbian.

One woman at the meeting said she is an emergency room nurse and would help patch Shelia up. She also knows a doctor who will help if they needed it, and the doctor will keep things quiet.

The woman looked up and said, "You can do that?"

The nurse got her coat, and said, "I will do that."

After that the women talked about the violence they and their friends have experienced. Some of them talked about how they wanted to be able to defend themselves. Several of them talked about just wanting to fit in and live their lives like everyone else. Others said that they have to stand up for themselves and stop the violence. Someone knew a woman who taught a martial art called Aikido, and she said the woman could come and give them lessons. They debated that, but eventually agreed to organize Aikido lessons for after the meetings.

Two or three at a time, the women left. That was the DOB meeting. Poor Shelia. She got beat up for no reason, for being where she was, for being who she is. Even if she is a lesbian, that's no reason to beat her up! What would Shelia and her friend have done without the DOB to help them?

As Pamela, Bruce and I were going out, Babs gave me a hug and whispered in my ear, "I'm glad I got to meet you, Joan. I've heard so much about you. Tell Stasia . . . oh, give her my best." She was blushing as she said it. Yanina, I wonder what was that about? Where had she been hearing about me? I guess she might have worked with Aunt Stasia at St. Vincent's? How else could they know each other? But why was she blushing like that?

What a night! I'm glad we went to the DOB meeting. I'm starting to learn how much I don't know.

Yours,

Joan

Joan to Yanina

October 16, 1961

Dear Yanina,

Yesterday in Women in History we reported on our group projects. Our group volunteered to go first. There was some squirming and eye rolling when we said we went to a Daughters of Bilitis meeting and that it is a lesbian group. We ignored that, and I tried not to squirm myself. Once we got into our presentation, the other students got interested, especially as we talked about the woman who got beat up and how everyone at the DOB meeting rallied to help her. One guy asked why she was on that street so late and alone, Rebecca said "Why shouldn't she be there? It's a free country."

The next group described going to a coffee house in Greenwich Village. A woman staged a reading of Charlotte Perkins Gilman's short story, "The Yellow Wallpaper." It's a creepy story, but there was something intriguing about it, even hearing it third hand. In the story a guy rents a cottage for the summer. His wife is trying to get over being depressed, he locks her in a bedroom, and she sort of goes crazy. (How would locking her in that room help her depression? More proof that you can never trust a man.) The woman thinks there are other women creeping around behind the patterns of the wallpaper. Then she thinks she is one of those women. When the summer is over, she refuses to leave the room because it became her sanctuary. Creepy, but I want to read the story.

The third group attended a lecture by student health services on something called 'the pill,' an oral contraceptive, like a vitamin, only it keeps you from getting pregnant. How can a pill keep you from getting pregnant? But, student health services sponsored the lecture, there must be something to it. I wish I knew about that pill last semester.

The last group attended a Student Non-Violent Coordinating Committee (SNCC) rally at the African National Memorial Bookstore on Seventh Avenue up in Harlem. SNCC organizes people to picket stores and places that practice segregation. Dr. Cobbe gave them her professor look and asked, "And how is this a women's event?" KarenMarie didn't even blink, she quoted the speaker who said, "To understand how society functions, you must understand the relationship between the women and the men. We have to liberate minds as well a society."

Dr. Cobbe scrunched up the right side of her mouth, and said, "Go on." The speaker, Angela somebody, impressed KarenMarie's group. KarenMarie's whole being lit up when she talked about her. She told us how Angela celebrated the proud African heritage of all Black people, how Black people in the United States fought to overcome slavery and are still fighting to overcome the effects of slavery. The government promised freed slaves forty acres of farmable land and a mule. That promise was never fulfilled.

KarenMarie quoted Angela, "Reparations are due to the descendants of those slaves. But what do we get? Not reparations but segregation." SNCC is calling on all college students to come together and work for the freedom and equality of all people, Black, Brown and White. In SNCC women are working alongside the men to wipe out discrimination. They are asking students in the north to join in picketing stores that have branches in the south that are practicing segregation, and they are looking for volunteers to help with voter registration drives and sit-ins and marches in the south.

The group also talked about another women from SNCC, Kiona, who was part of a march where the police came and set their dogs on the marchers and one dog bit Kiona's leg. The closest hospital was for white people and they refused to treat her. She had to go to the hospital for Negroes on the other side of town, and she almost bled to death during the drive. Kiona still walks with a limp because there was permanent damage to her leg muscle. Angela said "don't volunteer because it sounds romantic, volunteer because you are fearless and you want to make a difference." Angela—Davis—that was her name, Angela Davis, also said Mrs. Roosevelt supports their group and their cause.

That KarenMarie is something. Part of me wishes I had been in her group. I like her. We talked for a while after class, and we are going to meet for coffee at Jake sometime.

But, back to class, after we all reported on where we had been and we all discussed what we learned, Dr. Cobbe asked, "What issues have we not addressed?"

Patricia piped up, "What about peace? None of our groups did anything related to women and peace movements or anti-war stuff or banning nuclear testing."

Curtis added, "And music. Protest music. Isn't there women's music?"

Rita said, "Women's right to work."

We brainstormed more issues: poverty, unemployment, homelessness, hunger, drugs, gangs, access to education, raising the minimum wage, and something Dr. Cobbe called equal pay for equal work. All that talking left me exhausted and hungry. But I am always hungry.

At the end of class, Dr. Cobbe said that becoming aware of issues is the first step, and she hopes we will each take up a cause as part of our life's work. She said one of her relatives in Ireland, Frances Power Cobbe liked to say, "Every woman who has any margin of time or money to spare should adopt a public interest, a philanthropic undertaking or a social reform, and give to that cause whatever time and work she may be able to afford." What a way to end a class.

Enough Barnard-ness. What's your tale, Nightingale? How is Simcha? I miss you.

Always yours,

Joan

Joan to Yanina

November 7, 1961

Dear Yanina,

Remember that note I got from President Barrows saying he wanted to meet with me? That meeting was today. When I got to his office, he looked at me like I was a bug to be crushed. He invited me to have a seat, but before I had time to sit, he said, "Miss Zatańczy, it seems you have made quite a number of unwise decisions. But, I will ask you, can you tell me why you should not be dismissed from Barnard?"

Yanina, I thought I would die. I could feel the blood drain out of my face. I nearly passed out. But I got hold of myself and said, "What do you mean?"

President Barrows listed off that I am living in unsanctioned off campus housing, that I haven't applied for graduation, and that I have not submitted the forms to record my senior thesis topic. Then he said, "These violations of College policies and procedures indicate a pattern of insouciance to College mores and standards. As I see you now, it appears that you are in more trouble than these violations of College policies. The college holds its in loco parentis responsibilities most earnestly. We require all undergraduates to live on campus to forestall inappropriate assignations. It appears that we would have done so with good reason in your case. I do not see how you now expect to navigate the waters of the academy in your condition."

I was in shock, but I said, "There is nothing wrong with my apartment. Dr. Smyth sanctioned it. He helped me to find it. Dr. Smyth said . . ."

President Barrows cut me off, "Miss Zatańczy, it will do you no good to shirk your responsibility or attempt to shift the blame to a well-respected member of the faculty. The college requires all advisors to report student violations of policies to me as President and College Dean. Dr. Smyth is clear on, and observant of his responsibilities within the College. I suggest you review the Barnard standards regarding off campus housing on pages 73 and 74 of The Blue Book. As you should know, we have compiled all Barnard rules and regulations into the Blue Book, our student handbook. You would do well to read your copy. Then bring your letter of withdrawal from the college to me, or I will refer your case to the College Judicial Committee."

That was the end of our meeting. He walked out of his office. I sat there stunned. Yanina, I could hardly stand up, but I got out of his office, collapsed on the steps of Millbank Hall, and sat there crying. I didn't care who saw me. I just didn't care. I don't know how long I was there, but when I looked up, Dr. Cobbe, my fire-breathing dragon, was sitting on one side of me and KarenMarie was on the other.

KarenMarie put her arm around me and said, “Oh, Honey.” Dr. Cobbe said, “Tell me.” And I did. I was blubbering and incoherent, but I told them about my meeting with President Barrows, and Dr. Smyth, and my apartment. I told them I was just starting to see a ray of light at the end of the tunnel—Legal Aid filed the paternity papers and they said we had an excellent case to compel Smyth to pay child support. Just when I am about to make Smyth take responsibility, Barrows is going to dismiss me from the college.

Dr. Cobbe spit fire and said that as my advisor, Smyth should have made sure my apartment fit the college off campus housing policies, especially since he was instrumental in my securing that housing. But then she kind of turned purple and told me she overheard four faculty members talking about Smyth being taken to court by an undergraduate he got pregnant. The sentiment was that as long as he kept his affairs quiet, the faculty would ignore them. But the potential publicity from the court case has awakened the faculty’s moral conscience. The timing of my legal action against Dr. Smyth and Barrows action against me is not a coincidence.

Dr. Cobbe and I will meet tomorrow to figure out what I can do. I don’t like having to rely on someone in the faculty to help me with this. Why would she take my side and not protect one of her colleagues? But I don’t know what else to do. I know it’s a risk trusting her, but I’ve got to find a way out of this, and I need help to figure out what is possible. She was the one who encouraged me to sue Smyth, she sent me to see Legal Aid. Maybe she is feeling guilty. I’ve got to find a way out of this. I am all tied up in knots with these college rules and faculty politics.

I can't get thrown out of Barnard, I just can't. KarenMarie stuck around after Dr. Cobbe left and we talked. She said she was wondering if I was pregnant. She has an older sister who has a daughter in fifth grade. Her sister wanted to finish high school before she started to show. KarenMarie says I have that same look about me that her sister had—desperate, anxious and hopeful. KarenMarie has a plucky wisdom to the way she sees things. I told her I was planning to keep the baby, but I wasn't sure how I could manage working and taking care of the baby after I graduate. She said, "Honey, I've seen people manage worse. You can do it if you put your mind to it. It's not easy, and you will have to make hard choices. Dream, struggle. Two sides, one coin. It if you want it badly enough, you just keep on working at." Yanina, she sounded just like Bubba!

In the meantime, I keep pouring through the letters from Mrs. Roosevelt to keep myself distracted. I'm sending you one. I've read it two or three times and I don't even remember what the letter is about. Something about something Mrs. Roosevelt said that she wished she didn't say, and about women being important to her. I guess we all do things we regret. All I know is that my life is a mess. So much for flourishing. Maybe the purpose of my life is to learn how to clean up my messes.

That stupid Blue Book does say that you have to get special permission before you move into off campus housing, and it has to be in an approved women's hotel or supervised residence. And you are supposed tell the Director of College Activities before you move. Man-oh-Manischewitz am I screwed. I didn't tell the Director of College Activities, my building is not on the approved list, and there is no way I can try to justify it as a women's hotel with Mr. Mola living right down the hall from me.

Eleanor Roosevelt may have said, "learn from the mistakes of others, you can't live long enough to make them all yourself." But it sure feels like I'm coming awfully close to making every mistake possible all on my own.

Now I have to tell Mama and Aunt Stasia about this. It just keeps getting worse.

And, just one more layer of icing on the cake. You know how I was looking forward to Dr. Fredrick's course? Well now I hate it. Last week Dr. Fredrick said we would explore a Greek Spa this week. That shows how pitiful academic humor can be. This week's class was about Socrates, Plato and Aristotle, the Greek SPA. For Aristotle the meaning of life is Eudaimonia (Greek for well-being or flourishing), which requires virtue, practical wisdom and moral strength.

But just when I started to get interested, Dr. Fredrick said Aristotle taught that thinking about the good life is not for young people because we are controlled by our emotions and don't have the experience or practical wisdom needed to understand what it means to flourish. Yet another reason for me to not trust emotions. And we haven't developed the moral strength yet either (I guess my night by the Cathedral with Harold proves that point). If we are too young to think about it, why teach it!

UGH.

I wish I could drop this course, it is a frustrating waste. But don't worry. I know I can never drop another course no matter how awful it is.

Always,

Joan

From ER to Eva

June 20, 1947

Dear Eva,

Congratulations on your promotion!! Administrative assistant to the vice principal is a commendable step up from working in the school's secretarial pool. I am delighted for you. Reading your news is always a bright moment in my day. And these days, with my work on the Nuclear Commission, bright moments are very welcome.

Last Wednesday, the Nuclear Commission's work on drafting a human rights document stalled on the language of the first article. The debate had been going on for hours, and the discussion had fallen into nitpicking. The document used the words 'all men' to refer to men and women. I said "In the United States, when we say, 'all men are brothers' we mean all human beings are related to each other. We are not differentiating between men and women. I consider myself a feminist and I would have no objection to the use of the word men as we have written it within the document."

I desperately wanted the debate to move forward, but as soon as I spoke, I realized I should have been more thoughtful and sensitive to the conditions of women in other parts of the world.

After I made my little speech, I reflected on how important women have been to me in my life. I remembered all the specific women who helped me to become much happier, freer, and more deeply who I am today. I wondered where I might be if it were not for Marie Souvestre, my dear teacher, mentor and friend at Allenswood. I remembered Esther Lape and Elizabeth Fisher Read who taught me so much regarding women's rights and have become my dear friends; Nancy Cook and Marion Dickerman my dear friends from the Women's Division of New York State Democratic party who co-founded our Val-Kill Furniture Industries with me and with whom I ran the Todhunter School. I so enjoyed teaching history at our school. Rose Schneiderman who taught me the importance of trade unionism, Molly Dewson with whom I worked for legislation to limit women's work week to 48 hours. And my dear Lorena Hickok who is much more that a dear friend to me, who was an indispensable support throughout my early years at the White House.

As I reflected, I recognized the ways in which I would not be the woman I am today if it were not for those women. Each one in her way helped me to more deeply understand the world around me, and my potential and abilities. Each of them encouraged me to take risks, to develop my skills and to expand my interests.

My relationship with each woman was unique because we were both women. Women and men are not interchangeable, they cannot and should not be conflated into one ambiguous category. The practice of linguistically conflating women into men was much on my mind as I was turning toward sleep last night. I wondered about wives whose husbands history remembers. Wives who have been rendered invisible. The wives of Hiawatha and Deganawida came into my mind.

Eva, in our world today we remember Deganawida as the great prophet and peacemaker who proposed the unification of the Iroquois peoples. We remember Hiawatha as a founder and leader of the Iroquois confederacy. But what of their wives, those nameless, noble, proud women?

I imagined them chastising me, "We the wives of Hiawatha and Deganawida, fed them, bore their children and nurtured their bodies and their spirits. We helped to shape their thoughts and their lives. History remembers our husbands as great men, but no one knows our names. No one remembers the wives' names. Yet, among our people, the strong Iroquois peoples, women were full and active members. Our lives were rich and complete. We sat in council and spoke with strong voices. Men needed the sanction of the mothers and grandmothers to become leaders."

Among the Iroquois peoples, women had clear voices in the process of decision making, they carried political power. Men's plans for battle and war had to be approved by the women. Women owned all the household goods other than the clothes a man was wearing. Among the Iroquois people, the very earth belonged to the women, all women had a full voice and vote. For Iroquois people, women and men both, marriage was a voluntary arrangement, to enter and exit as they saw fit. Do you know Eva, there are some who say Miss Lucretia Mott, met with the women of the Seneca Indians Reservation before the Seneca conference. There are some people who believe the men who wrote our constitution studied the governance practices of the Iroquois.

It is good to remember that before the women's conference at Seneca Falls was even a twinkle in anyone's eye, the women of the Iroquois Nation were electing their leaders, and the women who organized the conference were aware of this. We who are leaders today, tomorrow and tomorrow's tomorrow must remember and give proper recognition to those who have gone before. Hiawatha and Deganawida were prominent leaders of their people. Both men worked diligently for peace among nations. Both men had wives who helped to shape their ideas and actions, through councils and over supper. Those wives had names which history has erased.

But, at the Nuclear Commission session I was tired and eager to move our work forward. I wanted to bring the debate to closure. The other women on the committee were right in their arguments, they were right in challenging my concession. To allow the document to go forward referring to "all men" would exclude too many women in too many parts of the world. In many countries men means only men. To not specify women is to abandon them and to ensure their exclusion from the rights we are working to detail. Too many women's hopes and contributions have already been diminished and lost.

Our discussions at the commission persisted. Finally, Hansa Jivraj Mehta, the delegate from India saved the day with her suggestion that we replace "all men are equal" with "all human beings are equal." It was an elegant and eloquent suggestion. Now we must see to it that women are no longer erased by pronouns, neglect or history. Eva, as we carry forward in our work, I will not allow any woman to be rendered invisible. Rather, I will open a way for each woman's name to be spoken and remembered.

Naming is powerful. We must claim that power. We must ensure the rights, protect and affirm the dignity of all people, both women and men.

With love, your affectionate friend,

Eleanor

Joan to Yanina

December 10, 1961

Dear Yanina,

You know how I thought I was in a mess? It is worse than I thought.

After my meeting with President Barrows, after Dr. Cobbe found me crying on the steps of Millbank Hall, she became my guardian dragon. I'm going to have to take a risk and trust her, because I don't know what else to do. When I got to her office, I figured out why she smells funny. Dr. Cobbe is a cat lady. She only has two cats now. She used to have five. She brings both of her cats to the office with her. Her office is littered with cat toys. She noticed me staring, laughed and said, "I come by it honestly. I was named for my late cousin, Frances Power Cobbe, a suffragette and anti-vivisectionist back home in Ireland."

She said an anti-vivisectionist supports science and research, but not in ways that harm animals. Dr. Cobbe brings her cats with her on her long teaching days. That's nice, but the kitty litter box needs changing.

Once we got the cat stuff settled, we talked about how manipulative Smyth is and how he abused his power as a faculty member. Dr. Cobbe kept pacing around her office with smoke coming out of her ears as we talked about how Smyth was seducing me from the minute I met him. I was a freshman and floundering in the big city. I thought he was being nice to a small-town girl. But Dr. Cobbe heard he does that all the time with vulnerable students.

And it gets worse. President Barrows is Smyth's uncle. Dr. Cobbe suspects Barrows is giving me grief because I am giving Smyth grief. If my paternity suit against Dr. Smyth were to go away, so would my troubles with President Barrows. But, if I drop the paternity case, I lose the child support Smyth should be paying. But if I don't drop it, Barrows will kick me out of college, and all of my tuition money will be wasted. What kind of job can I get without a college degree? I can't support myself and a baby on Kelly Girl wages.

As we talked about it, I said, "But that's blackmail."
Dr. Cobbe shook her head and said, "It is a bit of a Cornelian Dilemma."

I asked Dr. Cobbe who Cornelia is and where she comes into it. She said a Cornelian Dilemma is when no matter what you choose, something bad will happen. Pierre Corneille wrote about it in his play, El Cid. I don't care what the dilemma is called, I'm just so screwed.

Dr. Cobbe and I talked like I've never talked with anyone else. We talked about what might happen if I kept the paternity suit, and what might happen if I drop the paternity suit and get to stay at Barnard and graduate. We talked about what might happen not only in the next couple of months, but years down the road. Dr. Cobbe said that what Barrows and Smyth and guys like them want is to keep women barefoot and pregnant. As we talked, Dr. Cobbe and I both settled down, and we decided I need to think things through carefully. There is a lot on the line for me.

Dr. Cobbe got President Barrows to give me a little more time before he refers my case to the Judicial Committee. But I have to answer him before the end of the semester. I don't know what to do. I try to think, I try to decide, and my brain spins. I am so screwed. I am screwed in every way possible.

Back at my apartment, I was so frustrated, I threw a book and put a hole in the wall. Now I have to get that fixed. I need to pull myself together. I can't afford my emotions going wild.

I have to call Mama and Aunt Stasia and tell them what Dr. Cobbe told me. They are already at their wits end worrying about my getting thrown out of college. How will they take hearing that I'm being blackmailed by the college president?

And, I have a paper due for Dr. Fredrick's class. Philosophy and the meaning of life are about the last things on my mind. But, if Mrs. Roosevelt could take on chairing that United Nations committee, then I can and will get this done. I will reason my way through it. Things did not always go smoothly for Mrs. Roosevelt either. In the "Callie House" letter I'm sending you, she also writes about how she let down her friend Walter White from the NAACP. I guess everybody has frustrating times. She also wrote something about me becoming introverted and losing my sparkle. I can't remember what was going on back then, but if all this craziness ever settles out, I will have to talk to Aunt Stasia about it.

Anyway, Mrs. Roosevelt's letters are showing me the key is to keep going. I will not let Smyth and Barrows ruin my GPA.

All of that, and I still need to get up to the library at Hyde Park to collect primary source material for my thesis. So far the plan is that Pamela and I will take the train up to Hyde Park, to President Roosevelt's library. Aunt Stasia thinks it is safer for the two of us to travel together. Pamela is doing her senior thesis on President Roosevelt's Homestead Subsistence Division so we both need to use the library. All of Mrs. Roosevelt's "My Day" Columns are there.

How hard could it be? I will read through them and take notes as I read.

Always,

Joan

From ER to Eva

October 25, 1947

Dear Eva,

As I work on various projects at the UN, there are days when no sooner does one frustration pass, but another larger one takes its place. At the moment Committee 3 has cleared its agenda, and I am able to see work on our human rights document progressing; but closer to home I find myself in the middle of a quandary.

I have been a member of the NAACP advisory board for some time. Indeed, Walter White and I have become dear friends over the years and I would eagerly help him in any way that I can.

But I am also deeply committed to my work here at the UN and I must give that my first priority. Our work on the human rights document is a careful balancing of positions and relationships. The tension between our country and the Soviet Union is palpable. At every opportunity the Soviets publicly chide us for the way we treat Negroes in our country. They vehemently and vociferously criticize our racism so much so I have stopped listening to the words they say and merely wait for Mr. Pavlov or Mr. Vishinsky to stop speaking. Then I offer my acknowledgement that racism does indeed exist, but progress is being made. I explain that scores of citizens and groups are working to put an end to racism, and for Mr. Pavlov or Mr. Vishinsky to suggest otherwise is hitting below the belt.

Last week, I chided them saying, that with maturity we in the United States have grown more humble and acknowledge that we are not perfect. Because we acknowledge it, it does not mean we love our country any less. What it means is we recognize that human nature is not perfect and we work to continue to learn and improve.

That is all to the good. But recently Walter White asked me to join him in presenting a petition, "An Appeal to the World" from the NAACP, to the UN General Assembly. The petition describes racial discrimination in the United States, detailing the ways in which it stands as a violation of human rights. It is a thorough, thoughtful, well researched, effectively written document. It is a document that would advance human rights work at the UN.

How I want to stand with my friends to support their civil and human rights. Theirs is a cause close to my heart. It is one for which I have worked long and hard. But I cannot agree to Walter's request. My participation in the presentation of that petition would damage the international reputation of the United States. As a member of the United States delegation to the United Nations, as a member of the committee working to draft a human rights document within the United Nations, I cannot compromise my position. My participation in presenting that petition would be fodder to Mr. Pavlov and Mr. Vishinsky. It would weaken my ability to carry the United States position forward regarding the human rights document and in other policy actions. Eva, it is difficult to have to choose between two heartfelt commitments. But my commitments on the larger scale have to prevail.

I tried explaining that to Walter. As I talked, I could see the exhaustion on his face. He was asking a friend for help, and I was spouting policy analysis. When I stopped talking, he told me the story of Mrs. Callie House. It was not comforting to either of us, but I expect it reflects the truth of our relationship more than either of us wants to admit.

Mrs. House was born a slave, died a free woman. She was in Tennessee in January 1865 when William Tecumseh Sherman issued his order for each adult freed male slave to claim 40 acres. She cheered when the Freedman's Bureau promised each freed man 40 acres and then wept when President Jackson pardoned the rebels and restored their lands to them, taking away the possibility of land for freed slaves.

Along with Mr. Isaiah Dickerson, Mrs. House worked for the ex-slave movement. Forty acres and one mule for three hundred years of hard work with no pay—that was not too much to ask. Mrs. House and Mr. Dickerson argued that if the government had the right to free the slaves, then the government had a responsibility to ensure provisions for them. Promises were made at Emancipation. They should be fulfilled. Together in 1896, they formed the National Ex-Slave Mutual Relief, Bounty and Pension Association.

Walter said Mrs. House was a power to behold as she held forth on the needs and the rights of the ex-slaves. She traveled all over the south talking to groups of freed slaves. She talked to people who were struggling to keep body and soul together. She listened to people who were turned loose, illiterate, bare footed and naked without a dollar or a pocket to put it in; people who were free but with no place to go for shelter from the wind and rain. She listened to people who were free from the man who once had the power to whip them to death, but still depended on that same man who now had the power to starve them to death.

Walter chided me saying that the United Nations grandly expounds on freedom from interference but for the ex-slaves that Callie House was organizing, freedom meant loss. The Ex-Slave Association gave them hope. They contributed monthly dues and helped each other with illnesses and with burials. They sent petitions to Congress. Their petitions went unanswered.

In 1899 the Post Office issued a fraud order against the National Ex-Slave Mutual Relief, Bounty and Pension Association and its officers. The Post Office said that the Association and the officers could no longer use the mail because they were collecting moneys for fraudulent purposes.

From 1899 on the Post Office kept finding ways to obstruct their work. They made it difficult to collect the dues that kept the offices running. They made it difficult to put out newsletters and notices to the members. But the Association managed. They struggled along. They used Wells Fargo and American Express. They used their brothers and sisters names. On August 1916 the police arrested Mrs. House. For 20 years she exercised her constitutional right to petition the government and taught other ex-slaves to do the same.

But the Post Office accused her of using the mail to defraud people. They sent her to prison for a year. By the time she got out of prison, the association was dead. Mrs. House was too broken and too tired to do more than take in washing and sewing. She earned barely enough to put food on her plate.

Walter said he told me this story to show me that his people have been losing battles for a long time. They might lose a battle, but the war was not over. The work was not over. Each generation continues to take up their tasks. He said the NAACP would find a way to get their petition through the UN bureaucracy and to the General Assembly. Eva, I am not sure if Walter meant to take me off the hook, to criticize my commitment, or to chastise my sense of self-importance. I do not feel taken off the hook.

Oh, Eva, I am sorry to hear your concerns about Joan. She has always been such a bright and ebullient child, I wonder what has curtailed her spirit of adventure. But children are resilient beings. As long as her health is good and her grades remain excellent, I would not worry overmuch about her bent towards introversion. I'm sure she will find her sparkle again in time.

With love, your affectionate friend,

Eleanor

Joan to Yanina

January 5, 1962

Dear Yanina,

I am infuriated with that whole mess with Barrows. I had to drop the paternity suit against Smyth to get Barrows to drop his threat to expel me. I could have pressed the lawsuit and gone to another college after I had the baby. But another college is not Barnard. My dream has always been to go to Barnard, to graduate and become an alumna. I want to be like Helen Gahagan Douglas, the first Democratic woman elected to Congress; Ronnie Eldridge, the activist and politician; Grace Lee Boggs, the author and activist; or Margaret Mead who changed anthropology—all of them Barnard alumnae. I want to become a Barnard alumna who accomplishes noble things.

I will not let them take that dream away from me.

One day I was ranting to Dr. Cobbe about Smyth. I told her he used to tell me I was out to lunch. She gave me one of her professor looks, then she said, "Joan, you are many things, but out to lunch is not one of them. You are bright as they come. Your understanding and analysis of what you read is remarkable. But, some of your actions are imprudent. That you can fix. You can attend more closely to the possible consequences of your actions."

Maybe.

But at least, the Barrows and Smyth thing is resolved. I asked the Legal Aid people to withdraw the court papers. Dr. Cobbe informed Barrows. The court notified Smyth. And I got a note from President Barrows saying that because there were "extenuating circumstances" I may continue at Barnard and to live off campus in my current housing.

I'm not sure if the extenuating circumstances are my being pregnant because a faculty member got me drunk and seduced me, or because my advisor gave me bad advice. But they became apparent once I dropped the paternity suit.
I am prohibited from ever bringing my baby to campus—as if she might be contagious. But I can finish college. That is what matters. I will make that count.

Barrows and Smyth blackmailed me. I'm furious that they are getting away with it. But, for me, that is less onerous than leaving Barnard.

I was in my apartment staring out of my one little window after I read the note from Barrows, and for one moment I felt like a fire-breathing dragon—I could feel the smoke coming out of my ears. Mostly though, I feel like a more like a beached whale than a dragon.

Making headway on my senior thesis feels beached as well. You know that whenever I get frustrated, I reread Mrs. Roosevelt's letters. Last night I reread the letter about a speech Mrs. Roosevelt gave at the Sorbonne in Paris. The State Department told her what to say, and things did not go well for her.

I'm sending you a copy of that letter with this one. I keep telling myself that if Mrs. Roosevelt could deliver her speech at the Sorbonne, if those French ladies René Cassin told her about can accomplish all that they did, then I can take on writing my thesis.

Always,

Joan

From ER to Eva

October 1, 1948

Dear Eva,

On Tuesday, September 28, 1948, a few days before the United Nations General Assembly was to convene, I delivered a speech at the Sorbonne, the former University of Paris. What a grand setting. What and honor to be asked by my friend René Cassin to do this. At the same time I was nervous. Most of the people attending the speech would be intelligent and articulate with prestigious formal educations. In contrast, I never attended college. Most of my education has been through my personal effort.

And, I was to deliver the lecture in French. One of my Nanny's was French, so I grew up speaking that language, but now I do not use it on a daily basis. I was feeling *un petit peu* insecure and intimidated. But, my father always told me that fears were to be faced head on, so I marshaled my courage and agreed to deliver the speech.

In preparation for this session of the General Assembly, President Truman, Secretary of State Dulles and General Marshall said I should challenge the Soviets on their abuses of the rights and freedoms of individuals within their country. Obviously our country is not perfect, but we are trying to be respectful of the people in our country and of their rights, and it seems to me we are better than most other countries in our efforts.

With that as context, I accepted René's invitation to deliver a speech at the Sorbonne on the topic of "The Struggle for the Rights of Man." I was nervous all day the day of the speech. Not only for the reasons I have mentioned but also because I was to deliver a speech drafted by the State Department.

Some people in the audience were noticeably disappointed in the ideas of the prepared text. My usual way of public speaking is to have four or five general ideas I intend to discuss with the audience, and when I am at the podium, I simply speak from my heart. That way I have more freedom to respond as I notice audience reactions —I put in something humorous to wake them up, or explore an idea more carefully if they look confused. But when I have a prepared text, I feel I must stick to that, and I am not at my best; especially in an instance when the ideas are not ones I fully embrace, and that was the case for this lecture. The text of the speech from the State Department was largely a criticism of the Soviet government. I agree the Soviets deserve solid criticism, but I don't believe a public scolding ever does much to change anyone's behavior. But I did my duty, and now I must live with the consequences.

My standing at the United Nations may be tarnished by my concession. And, that I regret, because I do believe that it is through our relationships with others that important work is more readily accomplished.

The next morning, I was sitting in my hotel rooms thinking about all of that when there was a knock on my door. René Cassin stopped by to share a cup of tea with me. As we talked over the prior evening, he described three of his mother's favorite French women. Ninon de Lenclos was a well-known courtesan and author of the seventeenth century. She held a salon in Paris that attracted France's leading politicians and writers including Molière and Voltaire. She is still well-known in France for her wit and wisdom. René told me that his mother is fond of quoting her, "More genius is needed to make love than to command armies." And "We should take care to lay in a stock of provisions, but not of pleasures; pleasures should be gathered day by day."

Anna Maria Von Schurman was a brilliant academic in the seventeenth century. Even though she was required to give her lectures from behind a screen because she was a woman, she built a network of learned women in countries throughout Europe and advocated for women's education, for hearing women in their own voice.

But his mother's personal hero was Madame Germaine Necker de Staél, a powerful thinker and writer of the French Revolutionary and Napoleonic Era. Like our Mercy Otis Warren her writings challenged the political leaders of her time. Both Mercy Otis Warren and Madame Germaine Necker de Staél helped to foment revolutions that changed the course of their countries.

Eva, it seems to me that my friend was offering me some not-so-subtle advice with his stories of these three French women who spoke their minds and helped to shape the course of history. At this point in my life, I believe I have earned the right and that I carry a responsibility to speak my own mind. I shall be writing my own speeches in the future.

Your stories of Joan and Yanina cavorting together over the summer are delightful. I can just picture the two of them nesting in the trees behind your home, reading poetry to each other. It is a joy to recall the freedom of youth. Be well my dear friend.

With love, your affectionate friend,

Eleanor

Joan to Yanina

January 9, 1962

Dear Yanina,

Yesterday Pamela and I took the train to Hyde Park. I was determined make some serious progress on my senior thesis. How hard could it be to take some notes on Mrs. Roosevelt's "My Day" Columns?

Pamela and I met at Barnard. We were going to take the train from 125th Street up to Poughkeepsie. We missed the first train, so we had time on our hands while we waited for the next one. We sat there people watching, then Pamela bumped my arm with her elbow and asked me how things were going, she said, "you know, with the . . ." and looked at my belly. I said I was fine. She laughed, and said, "sure, FINE: floundering, imperiled, neurotic, eremitic. You don't have to do this on your own. Maybe it's time to let some people into your life. Bruce, KarenMarie and I are here and ready to help you. You just need to let us in a little."

Yanina, floundering, imperiled, neurotic, eremitic. Pamela has a way with words. And with seeing people. I am floundering and imperiled. I just keep doing the next thing that I have to do to keep my head above the waters of this Schits Creek I'm drowning in. Maybe I am a little neurotic. I didn't think anyone else noticed.

Pamela reminded me that Barnard is a small campus and some of the girls see my obsession with my 4.0 as kind of neurotic. Neurotic! Really! I had to ask Pamela about eremitic (Pamela is like a walking dictionary). Eremitic means a hermit or recluse. That started us talking. We talked all the way to Poughkeepsie. Maybe I could use some friends.

By the time we got to the library it was mid-afternoon. The research staff there were really helpful, especially when I showed them the letter from Mrs. Roosevelt. One of them took Pamela to President Roosevelt's Homestead Subsistence Division files. Mrs. Ireland took me to the file drawers with Mrs. Roosevelt's "My Day" Columns.

All the columns are filed in chronological order. Mrs. Ireland was apologetic that they are not indexed. She said they are hoping to get an intern to work on that and wondered if I might be interested in applying. Then she noticed my belly, and said she would leave me to my work, and to please refile any columns I read in the proper chronological order.

I stood there staring at the file cabinets. A wall of nine file cabinets. One drawer per year, four drawers per cabinet, seven file cabinets already filled and two extras for future columns. I stood there staring. I didn't know how or where to begin. I wanted to cry.

But all around me people were busy at work doing their research; research they knew how to do.

I didn't realize how many "My Day" Columns Mrs. Roosevelt had written! She wrote that column six days a week every week since 1935. 8400 columns. At 500 words per column that is 4,200,000 words. My English Literature professor says there are about 300 words on a page, so 14,000 pages, practically 50 novels.

Yanina, what have I gotten myself into?

I walked to the first file cabinet and took out the first folder. I sat at a table immobilized, staring at that folder. Then I remembered Mrs. Roosevelt didn't start to work at the United Nations until 1946. I thought that could be a place to start. Then I remembered Mrs. Roosevelt's letter describing her trip to the first United Nations meeting, and the "My Day" Column she wrote before she set out for England. I took out the December 1945 columns and found the column I was looking for. Then I started reading columns from January 1946.

I've been so distracted with Barrows threatening to throw me out of Barnard, I haven't been thinking clearly. I should have had a plan. As I stared at the "My Day" folders, thinking things through helped me to focus. I started to feel better as I got into the work.

As I kept thinking, I remembered I also had to find columns related to other Homestead Projects and Mrs. Bertha Brodsky. My head was pounding. Then I remembered that Mrs. Roosevelt would have written to Mrs. Brodsky before she and Mama started to write. I remembered that it was when Mama read about Mrs. Roosevelt's work with Arthurdale that she got the idea to have the sewing circle write to Mrs. Roosevelt. I was on to something. That would have been around when Mama and Papa moved to Roosevelt in 1939. I will need to read the columns before then and between 1945 and the end of 1948 when the United Nations ratified the Declaration of Human Rights. That narrows it to 6 years. Only one and a half file cabinets, not seven.

Just as I got that figured out, Mrs. Ireland said it was 4:45 and the library would close in 15 minutes. I was just getting started. Dr. Cobbe is right, I need to think things through before I jump in with both feet. Especially now that I can't even see my feet.

Yanina, one day at the library and all I have to show for my work is four pages of notes on two months of columns. Two months down, 70 more to go. At this rate it will take me more than a month to go through all the columns.
Speaking of "My Day" Columns, Mrs. Roosevelt had something hopeful to say about avoiding nuclear war. She said people in other countries are as anxious about it as we are in the United States. So, it should be possible find diplomatic ways to work for peace.

There is a shred of hope for the New Year.

When I woke up this morning, I decided that if Mrs. Roosevelt could accomplish all that she did, I can get this done too. I made myself a plan. Pamela and I will return to Hyde Park for three days. Pamela will come here Sunday night. We will borrow Aunt Stasia's car and leave by 5 AM Monday morning. We will be there to open the library at 8:45. I will ask Mama to pack us sandwiches and coffee. We will have three days of solid work time. We need to get the trip in before the semester starts in February, and before I have the baby which I hope will be soon.

I have my plan. No short cuts. I will do it right. First, I will start with the years between 1935, when Mrs. Roosevelt started her "My Day" Column, through 1939. I will look at the titles and scan the first and last paragraphs looking for information about Arthurdale or other Homesteads towns. If my work is going well, I might include 1940. Then I will have two days to go through 1945 to 1948 looking for columns addressing Mrs. Roosevelt's work at the United Nations. Aunt Stasia suggested I could compare what she wrote in the columns and what she wrote in the letters to Mama as public and private perspectives in my thesis.

Mrs. Roosevelt says, "It takes as much energy to wish as it does to plan." Now I have a plan. Next week I will put it into action.

Mama and Aunt Stasia send their love. Mama and Aunt Stasia are going ape for a new show on the television "Your First Impression." YES, we got our first television! Bill Leyden is the MC, Dennis Burbank will be a regular. They have a panel of three celebrities. The host gives the celebrities clues and they try to guess who the mystery guest is. Bubba told them that the former vice president, Richard Nixon, will be a guest and now the three of them watch it every day during their lunch break.

So, what's your tale, Nightingale? Please write and tell me the news from your kibbutz.

Yours, Always,

Joan

Joan to Yanina

February 2, 1962

Dear Yanina,

Spring Semester starts in two weeks, and I am due any day now. Finally. The last nine months have been the longest months of my life. I am so ready to deliver this baby. Deliver. Who am I going to deliver the baby to? A baby is not a newspaper. Should I say I will free the baby? Or expel the baby? Whatever I am about to do, I am ready to do it. Except I'm scared. I've heard stories about women and labor, the cramps, the pain, the labor going on forever. Ugh. I don't want to imagine it. I want this baby out. I want to get back to normal. And I know everything will be different, it will be a new normal. And I know I don't get it yet. I get that. But I am ready to find out.

I laughed when I read your Kasefet stages of a project. My moment of widespread unfettered enthusiasm where euphoria built, and all was glorious and right got cut short by Smyth's obstructionism. Reality reared its ugly head, disillusionment and disappointment quickly set in with Smyth creating problems, obstacles and difficulties. At Kasefet you head to Jerusalem's Western Wall to wail. I wallowed in chaos and panic. Then I re-defined my goals and developed strategies. I was ready to finish taking notes on the "My Day" Columns and dig in to processing my notes, write, edit, and revise my final paper. I had a grand plan. I was determined. I had it made in the shade. What could go wrong? Everything, that's what. Now I am back to chaos and panic.

Pamela and I planned out every detail of the trip to Hyde Park, with KarenMarie cheering us on, and Bruce pouting because he was not invited. We went to the American Automobile Association, and they made up a Triptik with our whole road trip laid out for us on 4 by 8 inch sections of a map with the pages all bound up in a plastic spiral at the top so we could flip the pages as we went along. We would not mess up our road trip the way we did with our train trip from Barnard to Hyde Park. We made a reservation at a motel near the Roosevelt Presidential Library. Pamela called the library to confirm the hours it was open.

The plan was all in place. Except for my secretly wanting to see Mrs. Roosevelt. Yanina, I really want to meet her. Since I read those letters from her, I feel like I know her. I want to talk with her and say thank you. I try to figure out Mrs. Roosevelt's schedule from her "My Day" Colum, but her columns say where she has been, not where she will be.
Anyway, it was a simple drive to Hyde Park. We got on Route 9 and headed north. We didn't need our Triptik, but this time I was leaving nothing to chance. We had our travel picnic, packed with plenty of food and coffee so we wouldn't need to stop on the way. Aunt Stasia put a note in the basket with a quote from Dale Carnegie, "Flaming enthusiasm, backed up by horse sense and persistence, is the quality that most frequently makes for success." She added, "Be persistent, Joan. And you too Pamela."

We were off to a great start. Four hours, three sandwiches, and too many candy bars later we were in Hyde Park. The Village Square Motel where we had our reservations was square on Route 9. It was nice, only a year old, everything was still fresh and new. It's one of those single story roadside motels, where all the rooms are in a semicircle around the gravel parking lot (they had white gravel—very fancy). We parked our car in front of our room and carried our stuff inside. The room had two beds and was clean and quiet. They had breakfast in the office every morning, and you could get coffee there all day. We were set. We were only a half mile from the library. It was going to be great. I only had to figure out how to get us to Val-Kill Cottage where Mrs. Roosevelt lives.

Since we had eaten ourselves silly in the car while we were driving, we set out to the library right after we checked into the motel. Pamela and I both got a decent morning and a productive afternoon's work done. I got through all of 1936 and 1937, found eleven references to Homestead communities. I was off to a great start.

After the library closed, we went back to the motel to clean up for dinner and Bruce was sitting outside our room waiting for us. He showed up out of nowhere. Actually, he took the train up from Columbia. He said he wasn't going to let the two of us have all the fun—like we were there to have fun. He was full stories about strolling along the paths around the old Roosevelt homestead that afternoon and how he heard someone walking in the woods singing "Fa la, fa la, fa la" like a crazy lady. I stared at him.

Yanina that was no crazy lady. That had to be Mrs. Roosevelt calling her dog, Fala. She was in Hyde Park at her cottage at Val-Kill walking around and I was inside the library with my nose in file cabinets.

The three of us had dinner together and then we let Bruce sleep on the floor of our room that night. It was a little strange sleeping with him in the room, but at least no one snored. The next morning we were up early, had our breakfast of donuts and coffee in the motel lobby and we were off to the library. Pamela and I agreed to meet up with Bruce for lunch. We figured we would need a break by then. Bruce was happy to do whatever Pamela and I wanted as long as we didn't throw him out for intruding on our research trip. I found six more references to the Arthurdale Homestead Project in the 1938 and 1939 columns. I had documentation that Jersey Homestead, now our Roosevelt, was not the only homestead project Mrs. Roosevelt was interested in. I was on a roll. I was feeling more confidence.

When we broke for lunch, Bruce was waiting in the motel room. He found a great deli and bought us each a pastrami sandwich (with pickles on the side) and chips. Bruce said "And, coleslaw, which as a matter of fact, is cabbage salad. You are slicing and dicing Mrs. Roosevelt's Columns. I brought you sliced and diced cabbage. Now all you have to do is digest it all and produce something insightful and inspired." Pamela rolled her eyes, but Bruce is really thoughtful (and kind of cute).

I like the way we have become the three musketeers. It is nice to have friends on campus. Yanina, everything was going so well. I was starting to feel like things might finally go my way, like I could trust people again.

It was warm for February, so I agreed to take a walk on one of the paths Bruce had been exploring, even though walking is a struggle for me these days. I was hoping I might catch a glimpse of Mrs. Roosevelt. Bruce found a picnic table where we could sit and look at the Hudson River and have our lunch.

Half way through our sandwiches Bruce pulled out a plastic 35 mm film canister. Pamela took one look at it and her smile got real big. Bruce said his cousin gave it to him for his birthday, he called it Mary Jane. Bruce pulled out some little cigarette papers and rolled some marijuana into a cigarette (he called it a joint). He lit it, took a puff and passed it to Pamela. Then she handed it to me. I wasn't sure if I should, what with my being pregnant and everything, but Bruce said it was good for cramps. Pamela said I wasn't having cramps. Bruce said, "What harm can it do?"

It seemed OK, so I took a puff. I didn't feel anything. We kept passing that joint around. We smoked one more and then another, and then the three of us were laughing. Everything seemed funnier than words. I never ate a pastrami sandwich as good as that one. Pamela said we had the munchies. That coleslaw was the best coleslaw I ever tasted! Bruce said that in India people offer foods to the gods and goddesses as gifts. He said Ganesha is a god with an elephant head and a man's body. Ganesha is the remover of remover of obstacles and a favorite of students. (Bruce and India and Hindu gods.) Bruce said he would offer his coleslaw to Ganesha and ask him to help Pamela and me with our research; he walked over and dumped his coleslaw into the river.

Yanina, when he did that, the strangest thing happened. It was like I saw the river for the first time. The sunlight danced on the water in a kaleidoscope of sparkling colors, sparkling into a web of light. I was one with the light. I was one with the river. Infinity danced through me, with me. Everything was so clear. I could see the river flowing, and the layers of the water, the fish and the rocks. More than seeing it, I could feel it. I was the river, I was the water, the blue bench, the green grass, the air I was breathing. I was one with everything. I was one with my baby. I could feel her heart beating. I was one with it all.

I breathed it in and exhaled it back out. We were all part of the same web, we all resonated with the same vibrations. The bench, the grass, the Pine trees, the river, Bruce's coleslaw, Bruce, Pamela, my baby, each our own note, all part of the same song. All of it, all of us, we were a song in perfect harmony. There was a sound flowing around me and though me, the sweetest harmonic unfolding in an unending vastness. It was all so beautiful. It was all as it should be. Everything was perfect, everything was the way it was supposed to be. The spirit of the universe radiated in me, with me, through me. There was no freedom or discipline, there was no this or that, there was just being: being and becoming.

I was in perfect harmony with the world, with the universe. I looked at Pamela and Bruce and they were beautiful, they were so beautiful I wanted to hug them both, but I didn't want to move and break the moment. I smiled at them. I wanted to tell them everything was OK, that it was all more than OK, that everything was exactly as it should be. I felt good about me and the baby and everything. I was floating is a sea of contentment.

Pamela looked at me and started to laugh. The moment was broken. She said the look on my face was pretty far out. I started to get angry with her for breaking the moment, but then we were all laughing together.

As our laughing subsided, I noticed that the sun was setting. We blew the whole afternoon sitting on that bench eating and smoking that stupid marijuana. The library was closed. We wasted an entire afternoon of research time. So much for Bruce's Ganesha removing any obstacles to our progress with our research.

We went back to the motel. Pamela and I agreed to call it an early night, get up early and be at the door when the library opened. We let Bruce sleep on the floor of our room again. What else could we do? We were all still too stoned to even think straight. We opened the curtains so that the daylight would wake us up. But Bruce woke up in the night and closed the curtains because the lights in the parking lot were bothering him.

Yanina, we all slept in until noon.

When we got back to the library that afternoon, Mrs. Ireland met us at the door. "Oh girls, we missed you this morning. Mrs. Roosevelt stopped by to say hello, she would have enjoyed meeting you." Yanina, I slept through meeting Mrs. Roosevelt! Bruce and that stupid marijuana. So much for trusting things to be going my way.

We only had that afternoon left, and I had the entire time Mrs. Roosevelt worked with the United Nations to go through. Mrs. Roosevelt wrote a lot about her work at the United Nations. I barely got through 1946 when they closed the library for the night and we had to head home. I had a grand plan. Smoking that stuff seemed like a good idea at the time, but now my plan is up in smoke. I am so up Schits Creek in a barbed wire canoe with no paddle.

Ugh. Bruce.

As we were driving home on Route 9 a blue roadster zipped past us, and I am confident, I am most definitely positive that the passenger in that car was none other than Mrs. Eleanor Roosevelt. I am sure of it. Pamela was looking backwards, talking to Bruce in the back seat, so she didn't see who was in the car. But I will swear to it, it had to have been Mrs. Roosevelt. I was that close and missed her. The whole tripe was a monumental disaster.

Today her "My Day" Column was back to nuclear weapons, this time about testing. She said Matt Shermer warns us that the 'fall out' in the atmosphere from testing those weapons is toxic. Mrs. Roosevelt and Matt Shermer agree that the United Nations should be doing something. But they aren't.

For my money, our trip was a monumental, resounding failure. I didn't get my research done, I missed seeing Mrs. Roosevelt. So much for being at one with the universe. Mrs. Roosevelt kept at her work on the human rights document until she got it done. Look at this letter I am sending you. She worked at it for years until it was finished. She was eloquent about human rights. Mrs. Roosevelt set out to write a declaration of human rights, and she got the document finished and approved. She even got a standing ovation for her work.

I keep making plans and messing them up. Every time I trust someone or get carried away with my emotions, I wind up regretting it. I think I am having fun, and then the bottom falls out. I have less than a three hour window of enthusiasm, horse sense and persistence. What is wrong with me?

You and Aunt Stasia both keep reminding me to keep breathing.

And to remember—nose →grindstone.

From now on, I am all about nose →grindstone.

Joan

From ER to Eva

December 12, 1948

Dear Eva,

December 10 is a day that I will never forget. The *Universal Declaration of Human Rights*—the document that our Drafting Committee of the Commission on Human Rights has been working on for so long—finally came up for discussion in the General Assembly. There were moments when I feared the entire process would be derailed. There were moments when it seemed someone might move to table the discussion and the vote until the next meetings of the General Assembly. I feared that a delay would permit a deterioration of the tenuous coalitions so many of us painstakingly built to support the document. But, just after 11 PM, the vote was called. With forty-eight countries voting yes, eight countries abstaining, and no one voting in opposition, at four minutes until midnight, the document was adopted by the General Assembly. It was a magnificent moment.

After the vote, Mr. Herbert Evatt, President of the General Assembly, closed the session by paying a most unexpected tribute to me. The entire General Assembly gave me a standing ovation. A standing ovation! I couldn't help but wonder what Franklin would have said. I wondered what Marie Souvestre, my Allenswood mentor, would have thought. If only I could have had those two people, who were so important in my life, with me that night. What a moment. So much hard work by so many people. Finally, we saw it come to fruition.

And, as wonderful as that moment was, I am practical enough to know that now the real work begins. Words in a document are a necessary step. But for those words to have true import and meaning, they must take form and shape in the day-to-day lives of particular people, of each individual human being, each family, each community that form the countries of our world.

Eva, as I write these words to you, it occurs to me you may not be familiar with the splendid document about which I am writing. Let me introduce it to you. If my dear friend René Cassin were writing to you, he would insist that our Declaration of Human Rights is but the foundation in an ongoing effort to describe the conditions necessary for human dignity. René insists our document must be read as a whole and integrated statement. He asserts that it will not do to look at any particular right or even a group of rights without remembering all the rights that have been delineated. Indeed, we may add to, but never delete from these conditions of human dignity.

Oh, Eva, you should hear René go on about the dignity of the individual within the family as the bedrock of all humanity. Our declaration is but a draft of the conditions necessary for human dignity to flourish. It endeavors to spell out the interdependence among human rights and the interdependence of human beings with one another and with our civil, social and natural environments.

René looks as if he is leading the charge to storm the Bastille when he extols dignity and his dear liberty, equality and fraternity as the four foundations of all human rights. We have borrowed liberally from the words of the French and American Revolutions in our writing.

Look at these grand aspirations from the preamble of our document: "recognition of the inherent dignity and of the equal and inalienable rights of all members of the human family is the foundation of freedom, justice and peace in the world . . . the peoples of the United Nations have in the Charter reaffirmed their faith in fundamental human rights, in the dignity and worth of the human person and in the equal rights of men and women and have determined to promote social progress and better standards of life . . . a common understanding of these rights and freedoms is of the greatest importance for the full realization of this pledge."

Article one spells out our firm belief that all human beings are born free and equal in dignity and rights, with reason and conscience. It affirms the importance of a spirit of common humanity in all human relationships. Article two makes plain the universality of these rights.

There are moments when I reflect on the Declaration that I envision Callie House and the members of the National Ex-Slave Mutual Relief, Bounty and Pension Association calling for the right to be free from slavery and torture; the right of all people, even if they are different in some way, to be treated like all other people; the right to be treated as innocent until proven guilty, and the right to receive help to claim these rights when you need help. These rights, to be free and safe from the things that governments should not do to people, are detailed in articles three to eleven.

There are moments when I reflect on the Declaration that I hear Mrs. Ishida and Mrs. Fujisawa and the Japanese people in the United States claiming the right to protection from others trying to intrude on your home; the right to have a home country and to move freely within that country, to leave and return if you want to do that; the right to have a family and to own things. These rights of individuals in relationship to other individuals and groups are detailed in articles twelve to seventeen.

There are moments when I reflect on the Declaration that I hear Mercy Otis Warren, Elizabeth Cady Stanton, Lucretia Mott and so many other strong women claiming the right to freedom of religion, thought and speech, and the right to take part in their country's political processes. These spiritual, public and political liberties are detailed in articles eighteen to twenty-one.

There are moments when I reflect on the Declaration that I hear Ninon de Lenclos, Anna Maria Von Schurman, Madame Germaine Necker de Staél, Jane Addams and all the women of Hull House claiming the right to develop and to use all the cultural, social and economic advantages in their country, the right to go to school, the right to work and to rest, the right to help when you need it if you can't work, and the right to share in the scientific and artistic developments of your country.

These economic, social and cultural rights are detailed in articles twenty-two to twenty-seven. And then I remember René reminding us all that these rights will only flourish within a context that recognizes the rights and responsibilities of participation in the social and political order. Articles twenty-eight to thirty serve that function.

Eva, we all have the responsibility to be aware of these rights, to build governments that respect and develop these rights, and to live our lives in ways that respect and develop these rights for ourselves, our families and others. Those are our next steps.

I'm afraid the history teacher in me has come out a bit too strongly in this letter. How I cherish my days at the Todhunter School. Those days with Marion Dickerman and Nancy Cook were invigorating.

These past days at the United Nations have been exhausting and heady. They have filled me with a sense of hope for our world, hope that this document will stand as a moral declaration and inspiration for people to work together to improve the lives of those who struggle.

Be well my dear Eva. All my best to Joan and Anastasia.

With love, your affectionate friend,

Eleanor

Telegram: From Joan Zatańczy in Roosevelt, NJ to Yanina Kominiarski in Kasefet, Israel

February 5, 1962

To: Yanina Kominiarski

From: Joan Zatańczy

Zayde in hospital. Heart attack. Condition serious. Come home. Details to follow.

Telegram: Yanina Kominiarski in Kasefet, Israel to Joan Zatańczy in Roosevelt, NJ

6 February 1962

From: Yanina Kominiarski
To: Joan Zatańczy

Received telegram. Making preparations. Will be home soon.

Telegram: Eva Zatańczy in Roosevelt, NJ to Yanina Kominiarski in Kasefet, Israel

February 7, 1962
From: Eva Zatańczy
To: Yanina Kominiarski

Joy Zatańczy, born February 6, 1962. Weight 6 pounds 7 ounces. Joan and baby doing well. Zayde in critical condition. Bubba beside herself.

Come home soon.

Airmail Joan in Roosevelt, NJ to Yanina in Kasefet, Israel

February 10, 1962

Dear Yanina,

I am home from the hospital with Joy. She is so small. She is so adorable; I hate to put her down, even for a minute, she is so precious and cute. She has the lungs of an opera singer, and when she is not happy about anything, she wails. We are up feeding her every two hours. I am over the moon when I hold her. I look at her and melt into a puddle of love.

But, Zayde.

Oh Yanina. Come home soon.

Here's what happened. It snowed a little, not even 2 inches. Usually Bubba can convince Zayde to wait for the boys down the street to come and shovel. But he got it into his head that he could do it. He got the sidewalk nearly done, Bubba opened the door to tell him she had Chicken Noodle soup for lunch and she saw him lean on the shovel, grab his chest and collapse to the ground.

Aunt Stasia was in the kitchen and heard Bubba scream. She saw Zayde lying in the snow and yelled to Mama to call an ambulance. Aunt Stasia ran out and made Zayde chew an aspirin. It's a good thing Aunt Stasia is a nurse. The doctors say Zayde had a nasty heart attack. He keeps asking for you and Avraham. Bubba did not want to bother either of you, but I sent telegrams to both of you. Avraham wired us, he will be here as soon as he can. Yanina, you need to come home. Soon.

Yanina, Abigail Adams said, "Great necessities call out great virtues." With Zayde in the hospital, we have great necessities. Now we need to respond with our greatest virtues.

Always,

Joan

# *Part III*

# *Spring Semester 1962*

Airmail Joan to Yanina

March 13, 1962

Dear Yanina,

I am back in school. And you are on your way back to Kasefet. It all happened so quickly. One Sunday Zayde was shoveling snow, he had a heart attack, and not even a month later, he is buried and Shiva is finished. Too much has changed too quickly.

Zayde didn't waste words, but he always had a good story, he was a great listener, and he was always there for us. He and Bubba were my first babysitters. Remember when we used to play in the yard and he would sit outside in his chair reading his newspaper keeping an eye on us? He taught me my first Yiddish word, *Zayde,* grandfather. He was the only grandfather I ever knew. After my Papa died in the war, he was like a father to me. When I came home from my first date, Mama and Aunt Stasia, Zayde and Bubba were in their front window watching. When I went to my senior prom, Mama and Aunt Stasia, Zayde and Bubba were in their front windows watching the sunrise and waiting for me to get home from the beach party. He was always part of home for me. And now he's not. But in my heart, Zayde will always be keeping watch.

I am glad that you and Simcha and Avraham got here. Having his family close lit up Zayde's face. I can't believe Avraham has been living in Israel for 13 years. I didn't understand why he came back to Roosevelt every year for Passover, until I overheard him at the hospital, "Zayde, you are my Jerusalem. You made a home for me that is my city of peace."

Yanina, this was classic. On Sunday Bubba realized Barnard's classes had started, she said "Enough has happened from those people to you. You will not give them reason to try to get rid of you again. Go now, study your books. You are the smart one. Show them." And Bubba gave me a note. She said she knew I collected these things. I opened it while I was on the train and there was a quote from Harriet Beecher Stowe, "The bitterest tears shed over graves are for words left unsaid and deeds left undone." Bubba wrote, "Between you and Zayde let there be no tears, only good memories for all the joy you brought to him."

Yanina, that is true for you too. You were a great joy to Zayde. Let there be only good memories for you.

Mama and Aunt Stasia are keeping little Joy for me while I am at Barnard, but not without a price. I don't know how long I can bear the look of disappointment in Mama's eyes. That look cuts deep because I am so disappointed in myself. Now that I have Joy, I have to get it together. Dr. Cobbe, Pamela, KarenMarie, and Bruce carried me through the end of last semester.

But if Smyth and his uncle hadn't screwed me over, I wouldn't have needed carrying. Trusting people is hard. I just keep hearing Mama in my head, "Never trust a promise." Why is she like that? From now on, I am all about figuring out the consequences before I jump.

I wish I could take Joy with me to New York. I miss her constantly. For someone so little, she takes up so much of my heart. I close my eyes and I can smell her—Ivory soap. But I am not allowed to bring Joy on campus. It isn't fair. But it is part of the blackmail deal, and I will stick to it. I need to put up with Barnard's stupid rules so I can graduate and get a decent job, so I can live my dream of being a Barnard Alum and doing something important.

Yanina, remember my letter about our last trip to Hyde Park? My first day back at school there was a mandatory convocation. Barnard does them once or twice a semester, and you need to get your attendance registered, because they have this 'community participation' requirement for graduation. It's good I got back when I did. I'm telling you I am not messing with any of the graduation requirement details. I am crossing every 'i', dotting every 't' and following all of their rules and requirements.

Pamela and I were at the convocation ten minutes early. We signed in at the Registrar's table and got seats half way back in the auditorium. You will never guess the topic: "Marijuana: Not for You." The guy had these posters with pictures of different ways to use marijuana. He talked about marijuana cigarettes. Pamela giggled and whispered to me, "That dork doesn't know anything. They are joints not cigarettes."

Then he started on about how marijuana is a weed with roots in hell, how using marijuana only leads to misery, and how using marijuana is the first step to heroin addiction. Pamela and I kept trying not to laugh. He said marijuana leads to orgies, parties and passions. Pamela said, "How did we miss that?"

The students in the row behind us were giving us the look, so we figured we better cool it. Sometimes Barnard girls can be so la di da. But really, where did they find that guy?

Here's something good from Barnard. Last week's Bulletin printed the new "Semester Reading Lists," and one book on the list is Lewis Copeland's *Popular Quotations for all Uses*. I can't wait to get a copy from the book store. That will be great for expanding my collection of quotes.

Bruce is taking a course on world religions and he read this book called *The Autobiography of a Yogi* by Paramhansa Yogananda. Now that is all he talks about. He does these weird exercises he calls yoga, and he says he is going to India, to Calcutta, to live in an ashram when he graduates. He wants to find that Mother Teresa he mentioned in Women in History so he can work with her. Guys can be totally weird.

I'm happy that you got to hold my Joy and to meet Pamela, Bruce, and KarenMarie. If KarenMarie's sister can raise a daughter on her own, so can I. KarenMarie is so committed to working for civil rights. It was energizing to listen to the two of you talk. Isn't Bruce good to Joy? He always asks about her and brings little things for her. I think he is infatuated with her.

Yanina, while you were here I never got a chance to tell you, but I remember that conversation between you and Aunt Stasia. She gets positively lyrical when she is in her Buddhist moments. I love seeing the glow on Aunt Stasia's face as she goes on about the inevitability of illness, aging and death as part of life.

She gets expansive as she expounds on the ubiquity of suffering; how greed, anger and ignorance cause us to suffer; how they are avoidable if we remember to be generous, compassionate and to work towards wisdom.

Sometimes I don't get what Aunt Stasia is saying about that Buddhism stuff, but after this past month, it is starting to make more sense to me. Zayde's heart attack, his only real illness. Bubba looking so old, so worried about Zayde.

Then Zayde's dying. Aunt Stasia's stories helped me to remember that you can get to the other side of suffering. You just have to keep going, especially when you are mired in the middle. But, knowing that in my head doesn't change how my heart is grieving for Zayde.

I have moments when I understand things, like when I was looking at the river in Hyde Park. Then it all evaporates like so much smoke. And then I hold Joy, and I am overwhelmed by my love for her. She is so tiny, and I love her more than everything. My heart could explode with joy.

When I hold Joy, I am aware of everything, her breathing, her soft pink skin, the way she smells like Ivory Soap; the way the wind smells as it blows through in Bubba's dill, the songs of the birds in the trees. She is my Joy. She <u>is</u> the meaning of my life.

Yours,

Joan

Joan to Yanina

March 26, 1962

Dear Yanina,

It's been a month since we lost Zayde. My heart still aches for him. And somehow the world goes on. Spring has sprung at Barnard. Everybody has spring fever, except me. I am stuck in winter. Mama says I have post party depression, because now that I have a baby, the party is over. Aunt Stasia says I might have post parting depression, at least I think that's what she said, because I am not pregnant anymore, and Joy and I are parted. Between being separated from Joy and Zayde being gone, I am just so sad.

After that storm we had last weekend, I guess I should celebrate—at least we are all OK. I heard on the news that it was a level 5 Nor'easter, one of the worst ever to hit the east coast. It was bad for three days. Rain like I have never seen. And wind. Mama said we should build an arc. Aunt Stasia said when the rain stopped we could follow the yellow brick road. I was relieved to be in Roosevelt to weather it through with Joy. But it passed and I am back at Barnard. I keep reminding myself of what Anne Bradstreet said, "If we had no winter, the spring would not be so pleasant: if we did not sometimes taste of adversity, prosperity would not be so welcome." A little prosperity would be very welcome right now, I'll tell you that.

I am at Barnard, but I long to be in Roosevelt with my little Joy. I try to study and she is all I can think about. I sit in class and day dream about holding her and rocking her to sleep. It is ironic. I thought being Joy's mother would be the meaning of my life. But I am seventy miles away from her. Mama and Aunt Stasia are mothering her for me. I talk to Mama or Aunt Stasia every day and they tell me how she is doing. Aunt Stasia always has a story to tell me. She says that she props Joy up in the crook in the sofa when she meditates. When she does her chanting, Joy turns her head toward her and smiles. She is calling Joy her baby Buddha Girl.

I miss Zayde. If I hadn't been so fat and pregnant I could have shoveled instead of him; if the boys down the street had gotten there sooner; if anyone else had shoveled instead of him, maybe he would still be here.

It's funny how I miss Zayde. When he was alive, I took for granted that he was next door, there when I needed him. Now that he is gone, I have an ache in my heart and the silliest things remind me of him. The other day I was in the Hungarian Pastry Shop on Amsterdam Avenue. They serve these amazing warm chocolate croissants. (I should remember to take a dozen home for Mama, maybe then she will stop scowling every time she looks at me.) The smell of them reminded me of the hot chocolate that Bubba used to make for Zayde.

I remembered how he would sit and smell the hot chocolate, how he would keep sniffing it, and only after the steam stopped swirling out would he sip on it. Then he made those slurpy sounds as he drank it. Remember how that noise mortified you, Avraham and I? Now I smell warm chocolate and I miss Zayde. I would be so happy to hear him make those slurpy sounds again. It's funny how you don't miss something until it's gone.

I wish you and I could have had more time together while we were in Roosevelt. I wish so many things. Aunt Stasia says I am too young to have so many regrets.

But, back at Barnard, Dr. Cobbe is now officially my advisor. Smyth is gone to California. Gone and good riddance. After I had to withdraw the paternity suit or get kicked out of school, I could feel my blood boil every time I saw him on campus.

I was so flattered that somebody on the faculty wanted to be with me, but he was just manipulating me. I have half a mind to write a letter to the student newspaper at Stanford to warn the girls out there to watch out for him. I keep writing the letter in my head. I just might do it. But I have Joy now. I need to think through the consequences before I do anything.
I haven't decided what I will tell Joy about her father. I have time to figure that out.

Anyway, last week Dr. Cobbe scheduled appointments with all her new advisees to review our academic progress. My appointment was four PM, on Friday. I was planning on heading to Roosevelt after my last class Friday morning. I've been going home every weekend to be with Joy. I figure that's only fair, with Mama, Aunt Stasia and Bubba taking care of her all week. I told Mama about the appointment and she said to stay on campus till Saturday morning, Joy wouldn't notice if I was gone one extra night. She meant to be helpful, but that was cold.

But, I was looking forward to my meeting with Dr. Cobbe. She carried me through all that craziness last semester, and I wanted to fill her in on everything that has happened.
As I walked to Dr. Cobbe's office, I thought about the first time I saw Withey Hall, and my first meeting with Smyth. Withey Hall looks like somebody's old mansion. The first time I opened the door to the building I almost fell over. The smell that came out of that building was raunchy, stale beer and dead squirrels all rolled into one ugly stink bomb. I was ready to turn and run, but the secretary looked up, saw the look on my face, laughed, and said everyone got bowled over by the smell their first time in the building. She smiled and asked me whose office I was looking for.

I said I was there to see Dr. Smyth, and she said, "Oh, him. His office is up those stairs. Be careful, all right? By the way, my name is Lila. You tell me if you need anything, you hear? If you need help, you tell me, OK?" I wonder now what she meant when she said "be careful." Back then I thought she meant the stairs.

Anyway, yesterday when I got to Dr. Cobbe's office it was still overrun with her cats, their toys and litter boxes. She pulled a cat into her lap and asked me about semester break, her way of asking me about the baby. I told her about Joy and about Zayde. She wanted to hear how Joy was doing. I think I went on a little too long about how adorable my Joy is, but Dr. Cobbe is a generous listener, and she kept asking me questions about Joy. She was sad for our losing Zayde.

While we were talking, Doctor Cobbe said, "Joan, 'Zatańczy' is an interesting name. Polish isn't it? What does it mean?"

I told her Zatańczy is Polish, and means will dance.

"You will. You will dance. I can see it in you."

Maybe that is what Mama means when she says she can see Papa's free spirit in me.

Dr. Cobbe asked me what I knew about Emma Goldman. I remembered her from Women in History. She was a writer, an anarchist and a feminist. Dr. Cobbe told me a story about a party where Emma was dancing her heart out, enjoying herself, when a man chastised her saying, "No agitator should dance, certainly not with such reckless abandon. Such undignified frivolity damages the dignity of our cause." His impertinence infuriated Emma, she said "Any cause that stands for beautiful ideals, for anarchism, for freedom from convention will not demand the denial of life and joy. . . If I can't dance, I won't be part of your revolution." Then Dr. Cobbe said, "Joan, like Emma, you will dance."

Yanina, I want my heart to be free enough to dance with reckless abandon. But it scares me too. Why does Mama think being a free spirit is such an awful thing? I wish I had stood up to President Barrows like Emma Goldman stood up to that guy. But, my college degree was at stake. Still, there are days when I could kick myself for giving in to him.

Dr. Cobbe noticed it was after five and said that we had better get down to business. We reviewed my schedule and my progress on finding primary source data. I had to finesse telling Dr. Cobbe why I had so little data from my trips to Hyde Park. I confessed to her that now that I have Joy, I didn't know how I was going get back to the library at Hyde Park to finish my research. She asked me why I didn't go over to the City Library and use their newspaper archives. It's so much closer.

Obviously the public library has newspaper achieves with Mrs. Roosevelt's columns. Obvious to everyone except me. I have got to get it together now that I have Joy.

Of course I am continuing to read Mrs. Roosevelt's new "My Day" Columns. The last one had hopeful nuclear news. The United States and the Soviet Union are having a disarmament conference in Geneva. I hope they get something done so we don't wind up blowing up the world before I even graduate from college. I want my Joy to enjoy a good, long life.

Yanina, what do you mean, Joy is not the only one Bruce loves? Pamela is not into guys. Bruce must know that, after our trip to the Daughters of Bilitis meeting and everything. Now he wants Pamela and me to come home with him. I think he wants Pamela to meet his sister. Bruce and I are friends, dear friends, but just friends. That's all it will ever be between us.

Your, Always,

Joan

Joan to Yanina

April 10, 1962

Dear Yanina,

Spring break is coming up soon. Soon I will have a whole week to be back home in Roosevelt with my Joy. And I need to focus that whole week on getting my notes for my senior thesis into shape.

I keep thinking about February and losing Zayde. There was something about sitting Shiva that inspired remembering. It is like Zayde's *Tikkun Olam*. I remember you and I sitting on the porch in our rockers on either side of Zayde. He would scratch his chin as if he had a beard, tweak up his mouth in a half smile, inhale, exhale so his nose hairs sang, and then he would start, "*Dziewczyna*, before every thing, before there was any thing, there was Ein Sof, our source of all."

And he would talk about how when the time was right, Ein Sof sent out pots and pots of yaish, all that is, our world and its thousands and thousands of things as a brilliant light. But, as Zayde loves to say, things being what they are, and Jewish stories being Jewish stories, there was an accident, and those pots fell and shattered. That light, our world's wholeness, was strewn into all the people, places and things. Yaish lives in all the people, places and things even now.

His point was that each person is born able to find that hidden light and to render it visible again. Remember how he would gather us up in his arms, give us one of his bear hugs, and say, "You were born able to find that hidden light, to make it visible again." For Zayde, it was simple. We bring wholeness and goodness back into our world by recognizing that light in each other. That is *Tikkun Olam*, that is healing our world. That is how to make a world where all Jews, where everyone, is safe. I remember how he would look at you and say, "Now you are my *Dziewczyna*, you are my little girl. One day you will be a *kobiecina*, a woman, then you will go to your Israel."

He said to look for that hidden light wherever we are, to heal what touches us most closely. For Zayde, that is how to make a better world. We tell our stories; we gather the pieces of our lives; and we gather the scattered light of Ein Sof. I miss Zayde and his stories. I miss his light.

And now you are in Kasefet, in Israel, following your dream, making the light visible. And I am here at Barnard, missing you and Zayde.

Always,

Joan

Joan to Yanina

April 25, 1962

Dear Yanina,

Last weekend I was home for Easter, I heard Mama and Aunt Stasia in the living room talking about the war years. After all the stories at we heard while we were sitting Shiva for Zayde, I really wanted to hear what they were saying, so I slipped into the room and sat with them. Mama looked at me, and said, "I was remembering . . . you were only a year and a half old . . . your Papa came home from work and sat me down on the sofa in the living room." Mama said she was afraid he had gotten laid off at the farm, but he said he enlisted in the army. She couldn't believe what she was hearing. She made him say it three times. She said she started yelling "How could you do this to Joan and me? How could you do this without talking with me first? How could you leave me alone with Joan? You could have gotten a deferral. You work on a farm. You have dependents."

I guess I was already a handful, starting to run, starting to talk, wanting attention all the time. Aunt Stasia remembered my first word was "Teetee." Auntie. Not 'Mama' or 'Papa' but 'Teetee.' Mama laughed, but her laugh sounded hurt. Mama has that same laugh when she says I always liked Aunt Stasia best. Yanina, my first memory is Aunt Stasia reading to me. I still love to listen to her read. My first memory of Mama is her saying, "Joan, no."

Mama said she cried for days, saying, “How could you do this to us?” But Papa held her and promise it would be all right. He would have the army send his paychecks home, so Mama and I would be OK.

Mama said she was worried about our boys fighting over there, getting shot and wounded and killed and she didn’t want that for him. She wanted him here, home with us, safe. Eventually she got hold of herself and told Papa not to be too brave when he was out there fighting.

Papa promised he would come home to us.

Tears leaked out of Mama’s eyes as she said, “He promised.”

We were quiet for a while, then Mama said that day was bad, but June 15, 1944 was worse. She had just put me down for my afternoon nap when there was a knock on our front door. She saw a Western Union man standing there and her knees buckled. She wanted to close the blinds and hide. During those years, a Western Union man came to your door for only one reason. She opened the door and took the telegram and stood there staring at it.

Bubba was walking home from the post office and waved to her. Mama didn’t look up or wave back. Bubba came to see why. Bubba saw the telegram, took Mama’s elbow and walked her into the house. She sat by Mama on the sofa and said, “Eva, you have to read it. My Janusz and I, we promised Bronislaw we would be here for you and Joan. We will keep that promise.”

Mama opened the drawer in the side table by the sofa, the one she keeps locked. She handed me the telegram: "The Department of the Army deeply regrets to inform you that your husband Corporal Bronislaw Zatańczy was killed in action in the performance of his duty and in the service of his country. The Department of the Army extends to you its most sincere sympathy in your loss. Because of existing conditions the body cannot be returned to you. You will be notified of the location of internment at a later date. If additional details are received, you will be informed. Major General James A. Ulio, Adjutant General, United States Army."

Mama said she felt like her life was over. Her Brony, my Papa, was dead and all of her hopes and dreams were dead along with him. She sat there staring at the telegram. All she could see was "Your husband was killed in action." Mama said she heard Bubba talking, but couldn't understand anything Bubba was saying. Her Brony was dead. That was all that Mama could hear. There was nothing else to hear. Her Brony was dead. She said the words kept echoing like cannon thunder: "Brony, Dead." She kept saying, "He promised he would come home to me. He promised. Brony always keeps his promises."

Everything evaporated for Mama in that instant. One minute she was standing there going about her normal daily business, tidying up the house, getting lunch ready, and the next minute her entire world collapsed.

Bubba sat with her on the sofa.

Mama said, "I can still see myself in my yellow cotton house dress. I can smell the flowers out in the yard, lilacs and honeysuckle. If I close my eyes, I can still smell my Brony, Lifebuoy Soap—sweet leather scent of carbolic—when he stepped out of the bath tub, cow manure when he came home from the farm. He would walk in the kitchen, I would sniff at him, he would swoop me up and say 'manly.' I would wrinkle my nose and say, 'man-ure.' And we would laugh. Now I remember laughing together and . . ." tears slipped out of her eyes while she was talking.

Aunt Stasia was living in New York City then. Mama did not want to call her at work because they would make an announcement over the loudspeakers for her to come to the office. Those days the only reason they made those announcements was to tell you someone had died in the war. So Mama waited until Aunt Stasia would be home from work to call her.

While Mama was waiting to call Aunt Stasia, I woke up from my nap. When I saw Bubba and Mama crying, I asked why they were sad. Mama said that telling me my Papa was gone was one of the hardest things she ever had to do. I turned 4 the week we got the telegram, so I don't remember much from then—Mama crying a lot for a long time, and lots of people coming over and fussing. I remember crying but not understanding what was going on.

Aunt Stasia said when she heard Mama say she had a telegram, all she could think was, "No, please don't let it be. Please don't let it be." But she took a deep breath, and said, "All right, I'm ready." Mama read her the telegram, and then everyone was crying, Aunt Stasia in New York, Mama in Jersey Homesteads, and me sitting on Mama's lap.

As Mama was getting off of the phone with Aunt Stasia, Bubba came over with dinner for us dinner. That night Bubba announced that she and Mr. would be Bubba and Zayde to me. Mama said Bubba gave her the look and said, "Mrs. this is Yiddish for grandfather and grandmother."

And Bubba said that even if we were not Jewish, the town would sit Shiva with us. For seven days Mama was not allowed to lift a finger. The Rabbi came and prayed with us. People from all over town brought us food, cleaned up the kitchen. They visited with us and took care of us.

Mama said she continued to believe it was all a colossal mistake and that any day she would get another telegram telling her that Papa was alive, maybe injured, but alive and would be home soon.

Then on August 8, 1944 the doorbell rang, and a man was standing there. I remember a strange man coming to the house, and Mama getting upset all over again. Mama opened the door, he and his uniform both looked like they had been through the war. She assumed he was a beggar, but she couldn't turn him away. His name was George Urbanovich, and he was the medic with Papa's unit. George told Mama he was wounded in the battle at Normandy and was sent home because of his injuries. He said the invasion was one of the bloodiest battles ever, the ocean turn red with blood from bodies that were washed out to sea. The landing boat Papa was in was hit by a shell. Most of the men in the boat died instantly and became part of that red tide.

But somehow Papa got himself to the shore where George found him. He was alive, but the sand all around him was red. George couldn't believe someone could lose that much blood and still be alive. But Papa was fighting to stay alive.

Papa made George get out a pencil and paper and he dictated a message to Mama. With his last breaths, this is what Papa said, "Dear Eva, you are the love of my life. I am so sorry that I can't keep my promise to come home to you. Please love our Joan for me. Tell her that her Papa loves her. I love you both, always. Tell our Joan that I died fighting for peace. Eva, now you must live life for both of us. Remember me with laughter and joy. You must go on and let new love come into your life. Goodbye my girls, I love you."

George gave Mama Papa's dog tag and wallet. Then Mama knew for sure that Papa was gone. Aunt Stasia said Mama was never the same after that. Mama never got over losing Papa.

As Mama told us the story, the three of us were crying. As I listened to her tell the story, I understood why Mama is so disappointed about everything all the time, and her not wanting to hear promises about anything ever. I wonder why she never told me any of those stories. It makes me wonder what else I don't know about my family.

At least now I understand why Mama says, "Never trust a promise. It will only break your heart." But Yanina, Bubba and Zayde kept their promise to us. Lots of people keep their promises. Dr. Cobbe kept her promise to me. KarenMarie, Bruce and Pamela have stood with me. Maybe it is time I get beyond Mama's broken heart. Maybe it is time for me to trust people.

Papa wanted me to know he died fighting for peace. There was so much more to Papa than being a free spirit who broke a promise. There is so much I don't know about my own family! Maybe instead of working so hard to not be like the ghost of Papa that Mama grieves, maybe I can learn more about who he was and what he was like. Maybe I will work for peace. It is time I stopped living my life trying to keep Mama from crying. It is time to become my own person, to become the best mother I can for Joy.

Yanina, I'm sorry I haven't sent you any letters from Mrs. Roosevelt in a while. I've been focused on analyzing them for my thesis. But here is a letter Mrs. Roosevelt sent to Mama around the time Papa died. Mrs. Roosevelt writes about what helped her when she was feeling sad. Did you know President Roosevelt carried on with another woman? I had no idea, but I showed the letter to Pamela and she thought Mrs. Roosevelt was talking about Lucy Mercer, who was her social secretary.

Men. You really can't trust them.

And, in the letter, Mrs. Roosevelt mentions a picnic with Mama and Papa. I have to find out more about that!

And, what do you mean about how Bruce looks at me? You are off your rocker. I don't need any more complications in my life. And he won't want an instant family with someone else's baby. I just want to graduate, get a job, and take care of Joy.

Anyway, what's your tale, Nightingale? How are things with you at your kibbutz in Kasefet?

Yours, always,

Joan

From ER to Eva

July 19, 1944

My Dear Eva,

My heart aches for you. I read your letter telling me about your dear Bronislaw's death with the greatest sorrow. Having met Bronislaw at our lovely picnic in Assunpink Park, I saw what a fun loving, kind man he was. I saw how much you both loved each other. You have my deepest and most sincere sympathies.

Eva, take the time you need to grieve your loss, to feel your sadness and to let your heart mourn. There will always be a place in your heart for your Bronislaw, but now it must be a different place, a place of memories rather than one of hopes and dreams. Cherish those memories, let them remind you of the love you shared.

We must claim spaces of solace for ourselves if we are to weather the danger of a crisis. The circumstances were very different, but one of the most trying times in my life was in 1918 when I discovered Franklin had been carrying on with someone else. We were living in Washington DC, and I found my solace in Rock Creek Cemetery. There is a statue in that cemetery by Augustus Saint-Gaudens. The statue was commissioned by Henry Adams in memory of his wife Clover, who committed suicide. The statue is formally titled 'Peace of God,' but most people know it as 'Grief.'

I was overcome with grief in those days, even as you are now. Different causes to be sure, but I suspect the emotion resonates in comparable ways as we each face our losses. Eva, I found much consolation sitting on a stone bench, contemplating that beautiful figure, standing hooded with her robe draping about her. At first, I thought only of myself and my loss, then my thoughts turned to the lives of all women, past, present and those in the future. As I thought of the potential of the women of the future, I resolved to find my strength to be of service to my family and friends, my community and my nation.

My hope for you is that you will find a place of tranquility and solace where you will find your strength to live your life committed to the values you hold most dearly. Perhaps walking along your town's lovely Assunpink Park's trails will lead you to consolation?

This is a terribly trying time for our country, with so many wives and mothers losing their husbands and sons. Wide spread suffering and loss are hard enough to bear. But particular loss, the loss of someone near and dear to you, that is another magnitude of sorrow. My dear, if I can do anything to comfort you at this terrible time, you must tell me how I can help.

I suspect you will read those last lines and be tempted to think about the roles my life circumstances bring to me. I do wear many hats as I go through my days.

But, Dear Eva, please remember that for me, the love of family and friends is most important. My public activities are merely ways I find to make the lives of those I love somewhat better. From the first letters that we exchanged, I felt we were kindred spirits, albeit in different circumstances.

But differences in circumstances are a minor concern. What is important is the heartfelt connection between us. I dearly cherish our growing epistolary friendship, as I believe you do. You must not hesitate to tell me if there are any ways I might be of some help and support.

My heart is with you in your loss. My deepest condolences, my dear friend.

With love, your affectionate friend

Eleanor

Joan to Yanina

May 10, 1962

Dear Yanina,

I have been so focused on Mrs. Roosevelt's letters about her work at the United Nations, I completely overlooked her mentioning that she met Mama and Papa, and they all had a picnic in Assunpink Park! Now I absolutely have to learn more about that story. The next time I am home, when Joy is sleeping, I'm going to make a pot of tea, sit Mama down and ask her. I know she is not big on heart to heart conversations, but she is softening since Joy was born.

Yanina, thinking about Mama and Papa having a picnic with Mrs. Roosevelt in Assunpink Park has me remembering another picnic in Assunpink Park. You must have been about nine, I was 7 years old, we were with Mama and Aunt Stasia celebrating the end of the school year. You and I were skipping stones into Assunpink Lake, and Aunt Stasia was laughing at a squirrel scampering around chasing another squirrel up a tree. She said the squirrel reminded her of her brother—wild and free and always ready to find adventure. I remember Mama said his wild freedom was what first attracted her to Papa. She said she was smitten with how feral and uninhibited he could be.

Aunt Stasia reminded Mama of a story Papa loved to tell about being raised by wolves, wolves who taught him to nurture his wild side. She said he always had a wildness in his heart, in his eyes. But then Mama cried and said his free spirit was what took him away from her, his free spirit got him to enlist and got him killed. Mama said anything that even hints at being wild and free scares her breath away. Then she told Aunt Stasia that I was too much like my father. She got quiet and then almost whispered to Aunt Stasia how Papa promised he would come home. Mama got kind of angry and said she used to believe that if there was one thing she could trust, it was that she could always count on her Brony to keep his word. But he broke his promise to come home, now she knows she can never trust a promise, not from anyone.

As I think about it now, that picnic changed me. When I heard what Mama said, I vowed to myself that I would never be like Papa, I would be civilized and tranquil, I would always keep my promises, but I would know better than to trust anybody's promises.

I remember now I changed that summer. I got all serious and worked hard to not laugh or be silly. I felt frustrated and angry all the time. I felt like I was trying to squeeze myself into shoes that were two sizes too small. Mama must have noticed the changes in me and written about it to Mrs. Roosevelt, and that is what Mrs. Roosevelt was referring to in that letter from October 1947. I was just 7 years old then.

How could eavesdropping on one conversation make such a difference? Is that why I always feel so guilty when I laugh too much? Too much fun got me into a boat load of trouble this year, but, but remembering that picnic has changed how I see things. Maybe I need to let myself feel more. I remember laughing and dancing. Now that I have Joy, maybe it is time to laugh and dance again, to let my wild child free. I want Joy to have a happy, light hearted mother. I'm already an unmarried mother. What else can go wrong?

Yanina, there is so much more to taking care of a baby than I ever imagined. I wish you were here so we could talk things over like we used to do. There is so much more to finishing my senior thesis than I ever imagined. But I am working at it every day.

Yours, Always,

Joan

Joan to Yanina

May 22, 1962

Dear Yanina,

I have been a woman on a mission, like Mrs. Roosevelt working on her human rights document. Her dedication cost her some sleepless nights, she had to choose among her commitments and she disappointed people she cared about. I've neglected my sweet Joy, and KarenMarie, Bruce and Pamela; but three or four times a week, I was on the subway, transferring lines, and then walking a bit to the City Library for two or three hours of work. I became something of a fixture there. I read and took notes on Mrs. Roosevelt's "My Day" Columns. Then I would take the subway back to my apartment where I collated, analyzed, and organized my notes; I compared and contrasted the material from the Mrs. Roosevelt's letters and her "My Day" Columns; I wrote, revised, edited and revised again. Finally I submitted my draft to Dr. Cobbe, and we got all the college approvals.

It is done. I have finished my senior thesis. I am on cloud nine. Getting my thesis approved and finished is huge. My thesis and the letters from Mrs. Roosevelt have been what I obsessed over, the center of my life for the past year. The taste of success is sweet. Now I am free to freely obsess about my Joy. I love the feel of her in my arms. I love the smile on her face. I spend my week looking forward to the weekend when I can go home to Roosevelt to be with her.

She is growing by leaps and bounds. She is only three months old and I can't imagine my life without her. Not that it's been easy. Three months of classes, studying and taking the train to Roosevelt every weekend has been exhausting. But, I suspect not as exhausting as the interminable nights have been for Mama and Aunt Stasia. Joy is up every two or three hours every night. They take turns feeding her—what a wonderful thing that infant formula is. But neither Mama nor Aunt Stasia has gotten a good night's sleep since she was born. We are all exhausted, but Joy is flourishing, she is 24 inches long and weighs 15 pounds. My Joy is three bags of sugar. Every time I see her smile, I melt like sugar in hot tea. Life is sweet.

Yanina, I have to tell you, I didn't love your advice about not writing to the Stanford student newspaper. Smyth is a king *chazzer*, and I am tired of Professor Pig drubbing my rights. Don't I have freedom of speech? But I talked to Dr. Cobbe. She told me to write the letter and put everything into it, how he manipulated me, how he seduced me, how he abandoned Joy and me. I wrote out all of my frustration and anger with a vengeance. But Dr. Cobbe said don't mail it because revenge is a dish best served cold. And I am not in a position for that kind of dishing.

Barrows is still president of Barnard, and I am still a student in his college. He has a lot of power over me. Once I wrote the letter, then we tossed it into the fireplace in Jake. As it burned I was supposed to let my frustration and anger go up in the smoke. Dr. Cobbe said it worked for her, so I gave it a try. I guess maybe it helped.

I hate to admit it, but it might not be so bad that I am not graduating next week. I don't have a clue what to do next. Another semester will give me time to figure things out.

Yanina, remember how we used to climb that big old oak tree between our houses? We would climb up that tree and quote Louisa May Alcott. Remember, "Far away there in the sunshine are my highest aspirations. I may not reach them, but I can look up and see their beauty, believe in them, and try to follow where they lead." I remember you looked up and saw Israel. From the minute you landed in Roosevelt, your first English words were, "I will go to Israel and help to build a country safe for all Jews."

Yanina, you were leaving before you arrived. You knew what you wanted. And me? I'm on my way, I'm making progress. I always wanted to get my degree from Barnard, and I am getting closer to finishing that. But now I can see that a degree is a means to an end. There are things I need to figure out.

Dr. Fredrick's course was frustrating, but it introduced me to different ways of thinking about the meaning of life. This past year has been a rollercoaster ride; but I'm learning—to trust people, how Mama is still grieving for Papa, why she is the way she is—I'm learning.

You have Israel. Mrs. Roosevelt has service and human rights. Pamela has studying to get her PhD in history. Bruce has India, yoga and Mother Teresa. KarenMarie has working for civil rights. I have Joy. She is more than enough for me. I used to spend all my time studying. Now I spend all my time thinking about her. I can't wait to be able to spend more time with her.

My thesis is done! That is major. I will write a letter to Mrs. Roosevelt to thank her and tell her I've finished my thesis, but I wish I could meet her and tell her how much her letters helped me, I wish I could tell her in person how much she means to me.

Somehow, someday.

Next week Pamela and I are going with Bruce to see his family. I think Bruce wants to introduce Pamela to his sister, Rhoda. That should be interesting.

My thesis is finished, and Joy is healthy. Life is lovely.

What's your tale, Nightingale?

Yours, always,

Joan

# *Part IV*
# *Summer 1962*

Joan to Yanina

June 8, 1962

Dear Yanina,

I know you want to work for peace. And your insight, that those Palestinians in the Deir El-Balha settlement are people too, is beautiful. But I have to ask you, are you sure you want to be crossing into Gaza every week? Isn't that dangerous? I get that you want to work for peace in Israel, and I get that Mrs. Roosevelt's letters are inspiring, especially this one I am sending you where she quotes her friend Emily Greene Balch. But are Jewish people even allowed in the Gaza? Please tell me you are not being crazy? If my sending you bag letters got you hurt, I would never forgive myself. Please tell me the people with the UN Relief and Works Agency know what they are doing? Is that really the best way for you to work for peace for Israel?

It used to be that I understood conceptually what peace meant; I understood it in my head. Now I look at Joy sleeping, and peace floods my soul. The look on her face—that is peace. The smell of baby shampoo, the taste of her toes—that is peace. I was watching her the other night, and I remembered something Elizabeth Cady Stanton said, "Love is the vital essence that pervades and permeates, from the center to the circumference, the graduating circles of all thought and action. Love is the talisman of human weal and woe, the open sesame to every soul." Joy is my open sesame to meaning and purpose, my soul opens in her presence.

As to school, the semester is over, and I've moved back to Roosevelt for the summer.

I am 22. What a difference a year makes. Last year I was infatuated with Smyth and I was just beginning to scrutinize the letters in that bag. Now the spirit of those letters infuses my soul. I am changing because of them. Now I am a mother, nearly finished with college. And, I will get to spend three entire months with my Joy. My heart is filled with JOY!
I want get a job to help with the extra expenses from Joy. Babies are SO expensive. Food, clothes, diapers, the cost of caring for such a little person really mounts up. Mama grumbles some, but she and Aunt Stasia buy everything Joy needs. But I can't let them keep doing that. I want to carry my weight.

Yanina, putting a pillow behind Joy's back was a brilliant suggestion. I tried it the other night, and it really helps. Joy is sleeping through the night now, so we are all sleeping through the night. You have given us the sweetest dreams ever.

KarenMarie calls me two or three times a week, to talk and to check in on how Joy is doing. She is a wealth of information about babies and how to organize your time and your day to get everything done. I don't know how I would manage without her advice and Mama and Aunt Stasia's help.

Bruce and Pamela came out from New York last week. Pamela hardly stopped talking about Bruce's sister Rhoda. Interesting. I'm not sure if they came to see me or Joy or for the Decoration Day parade and picnic. They are both so good with Joy. She is such a charmer. She smiles and the room lights up. Bruce dotes on her. He brought her the cutest pink teddy bear. And before you even think anything else, let me tell you, when it comes to Bruce and Joy, he only has eyes for her. Bruce and Pamela loved the klezmer marching bands in the parade. Pamela stood there staring. I don't know what she imagined when I was telling her about the klezmer doo-wop group you and I started in high school.

The picnic in the green after the parade was Roosevelt at its best. There were tables and tables with all the classic Roosevelt covered dishes. There were platters of meat loaf, beef short ribs, and fried chicken, there were bowls of chili: sweet or spicy, with or without meat. There were green bean casseroles with those crispy onion things, broccoli salad, deviled eggs, five bean salad, Jell-O salads with or without fruit and with or without sour cream, two kinds of coleslaw, three kinds of potato salad, too many kinds of macaroni salad, cucumber and tomato salad, watermelon and cucumber salad, carrot salad and Waldorf salad. There were three tables covered with deserts—angel food cake, devil's food cake, apple cake; Cracker Jack pretzel treats, brownies, Toll House cookies, oatmeal cookies, peanut butter cookies, apple, cherry, rhubarb, and lemon meringue pies. We all ate until we all looked pregnant! Bruce had to taste everything. I don't know where he puts it. He isn't skinny, but he is not heavy either. He is the perfect weight, but he can out eat even me.

Yanina, I haven't lost any of the weight I put on with Joy. I need to do a lot more of eating a lot less.

After the picnic Mama and Aunt Stasia took Joy home. Pamela, Bruce and I walked the circuit, down Homestead to Pine Drive, Tamara to Rochdale and back to Homestead. Mrs. Lachman at the end of Homestead still has those incredible rosemary hedges. Roses still line Pine Drive, from Mrs. Appel's reds and pinks to Mrs. Landau's yellows and whites. Mr. Martin's jazz still provides the soundtrack for all of Tamara Drive. You can imagine how quietly we strolled down Rochdale Avenue past Mr. Wittlin's, avoiding an impromptu poetry reading. As we strolled down Rochdale, the vegetable gardens blew Bruce away. Sara was out in her yard grinding horseradish roots. Between that and her lilacs it was a battle of the noses. Then home to Bubba's blooming dill. Once we all stopped weeping from the horseradish fumes, Bruce and Pamela noticed how all the houses are the same. In New York every building has multiple stories and you can hardly see the sky. In our dear little Roosevelt, all our homes are still Bauhaus after Bauhaus, flat roof after flat roof, two hundred Bauhaus homes in one little town.

As we walked the circuit, I told Bruce and Pamela that if they were going to understand our Roosevelt, they needed to hear the Roosevelt Catechism.

"Who made our town (AKA 'Who made you')?" "Benjamin Brown."

"Why did Benjamin Brown make our town?" "Mr. Brown made our town to save Jewish Garment workers from the vagaries of seasonal work through farm, factory and retail co-ops."

Of course I had to tell Bruce and Pamela how in fourth grade we learned that when President Roosevelt announced the Subsistence Homesteads program, Mr. Brown applied for half a million dollars to create Jersey Homesteads, and in 1933 the federal government approved his application, but said he had to set up a Board of Directors to get their final approval. Somehow he got Albert Einstein, who was living in Princeton, to agree to be a board member. Fanny still says he tried to get Mrs. Roosevelt to be on the board. That would have been something. One thing for sure, Mrs. Roosevelt has a powerful connection to our town.

Bruce loved that Roosevelt is seven miles south east of Grover's Mill where the Martians landed in 1938. Even if it was only in the Mercury Theatre Company reading H. G. Wells' "War of the Worlds".

Then we went to the school to see the mural. They were speechless when they saw all twelve feet by forty-five feet of our mural—which I told them is actually a fresco. Bruce laughed and said, "Fresca? You mean it's painted with soda?" You would have been proud of me. I channeled Mrs. Weisberg and told them how frescos are a special kind of mural painted on wet plaster so the pigments dissolve into the plaster. Then I showed them the three sections of the mural, with each section symbolic of the Jewish experience in the United States: oppression, deliverance and redemption.

I tried to show them the Roosevelt Elementary School student secret. I told them if they looked carefully at the family in the top right of the third panel, the mother is Mrs. Eleanor Roosevelt. I told them you have to look carefully, if you look just right, it's her, right there, holding a baby in her arms. But they couldn't see her.

Anyway, Pamela found Albert Einstein in the second panel. Bruce recognized Heywood Broun from WOR Newark Radio in the third panel, and that was all the excuse I needed to launch into my favorite Broun quotes. Remember, "The ability to make love frivolously is the chief characteristic which distinguishes human beings from beasts," that was my favorite quote right after that night by the Cathedral. Now not so much. Yanina, my always, all-time favorite quote from Mr. Broun is still, "I doubt whether the world holds a more soul-stirring surprise than the first adventure with ice cream."

Once they heard that quote we had to have some of our Jersey Maid ice cream. I had a great big scoop of chocolate, Bruce had two scoops of peach with big old hunks of fresh peaches, and Pamela had a small scoop of cherry with those big black Bing cherries. Every adventure with ice cream is soul-stirring, thank you Mr. Broun. Yanina, do you have ice cream on the kibbutz?

You will love this. After the parade, there was a Klezmer Battle of the Bands on the town green. It was amazing how many versions of Hava Nagila the different bands performed—Rebbe and his group did a jazz scat version. And, Yanina, the winner of the Best Overall Klezmer Band? A Klezmer Doo-Wop group, the DooKlez. They won for their rendition of the Beer Barrel Polka. You should have heard them.

Roll out the barrel, shoo bop shoo wop, we'll have a barrel of fun, bop bop shoo wop

Roll out the barrel, shoo bop shoo wop, we've got the blues on the run, bop bop shoo wop

Zing boom tararrel, shoo bop shoo wop, ring out a song of good cheer bop bop shoo wop

Now's the time to roll the barrel, shoo bop shoo wop, for the gang's all here.

Some bands did traditional klezmer stuff, but it must have been a doo-wop day, because there were renditions of Peggy Lee's "I Only Have Eyes for You," Frankie Lymon's "Why Do Fools Fall in Love," and Mel Tormé's "Blue Moon."

For the grand finale, all the groups did a klezmer version of the Dell's "Oh What a Night." It was quite the night, with Bruce, Pamela and me and all the other kids from Roosevelt singing along with the doo-wop. And all of Roosevelt singing along with the traditional klezmer. What a night. It was nice to feel happy and free for a night.

Always,

Joan

From ER to Eva

January 22, 1953

Dear Eva,

These have been momentous days for me. My life is in a state of transition and upheaval, and yet it remains much the same. The day after Dwight Eisenhower was elected president, I wrote to the State Department advising them I would tender my resignation to the United Nations and the Human Rights Commission, as is the practice after the election of a new president.

On December 30 I received a brief note from General Eisenhower thanking me for my service and accepting my resignation. I replied to him I would in fact formally resign when he became president.

On January 20, after General Eisenhower's inauguration, I did resign. And, on my way home from posting the letter, I stopped by the offices of the American Association for the United Nations (AAUN) and asked them if they could use me as a full-time volunteer.

The closing of a mail box opened a door and a new chapter in my lifelong commitment to service and peace. I believe the United Nations is the single most promising way to work for peace. But I also recognize that too many individuals in our country do not understand the promise of the United Nations, and failing in that understanding, I worry that they may oppose our country's full participation in the programs of the UN. In my role with the AAUN, I will continue my work for peace and dignity as we educate others about the functions and importance of the UN.

As I was walking home from the AAUN, I thought about other women I have known who have worked for peace, and my dear friend Emily Greene Balch came to mind. Eva, in 1946, only a year after Franklin died, Emily was awarded the Nobel Peace Prize. How I wish Franklin had been in office to acknowledge Emily's work. But Truman would have none of it. He regarded anyone involved with the Women's International League for Peace and Freedom as too radical to cast their shadow across the doors of the White House.

Our dear Emily had more than her share of professional struggles. In 1919 she was on leave from Wellesley College and put in to extend her leave to continue her work with the International Congress of Women. The Board of Trustees at Wellesley choose to terminate her contract instead. Eva, Emily was a popular professor and one of the more productive scholars on the faculty. But, I suspect she was a bit too outspoken an advocate of peace for those men. I suspect they were looking for an excuse to be rid of her.

Emily was disconsolate—for a moment. But then she marched herself to the Women's International League for Peace and Freedom, much as I did with the American Association for the United Nations. WILPF elected her their secretary and treasurer, and she continued her work for peace with vigor, even though her health was declining.

Eva, as I remembered Emily, I wanted to reread her Nobel Prize Lecture, *Toward Human Unity or Beyond Nationalism,* which she delivered on April 7, 1948. Here is my favorite passage from that lecture. She discusses the peace movement in its individual and political efforts, its work to educate and to build institutions and to influence governmental action on concrete issues. I find great solace and direction in her comments:

*We are not asked to subscribe to any utopia or to believe in a perfect world just around the corner. We are asked to be patient with necessarily slow and groping advance on the road forward, and to be ready for each step ahead as it becomes practicable. We are asked to equip ourselves with courage, hope, readiness for hard work, and to cherish large and generous ideals.*

Eva, I will enter this new chapter in my life with courage and hope, ready for hard work, open to joy where it may shine, cherishing the ideals of service and human rights based on respect for human dignity.

And it appears I am not the only one approaching a new chapter in life. Your Joan is already making plans for college and she is only in seventh grade? Oh my, you do have your hands full. And, yes there is hope that she will set her sights on other schools. Barnard is a fine college, but there are other excellent schools she might consider as well. Smith College in Massachusetts is a very fine school and is in a much less urban environment.

With love, your affectionate friend,

Eleanor

Joan to Yanina

June 26, 1962

Dear Yanina,

Pamela and Bruce came out to Roosevelt again last weekend. They said to say hello. We all got to talking, and we were wondering, if both men and women serve in the Israeli Defense Services, how do they work out where people sleep? There must be people in Kasefet who served in the Defense Services that you could ask. And, how do you work out housing at Kasefet? How is that all organized? None of us could get our heads around it all works.

While we were talking, Mama walked into the kitchen, and Pamela started talking with her. Bruce joined in and said, "Mrs. Zatańczy, all these years you have been writing to Mrs. Roosevelt, did you ever get to meet her?"

Mama hesitated, but said, "There was one time."

Bruce pulled out a chair for Mama, Pamela handed her a cup of tea, and together they said, "Tell us. What was she like?"

I held my breath. But Mama sat down, sipped her tea, and told us the story of the picnic at Assunpink Park that Mrs. Roosevelt mentioned in her condolence letter.

Mama said September 25, 1940 was a day she will never forget. She said, "Joan, you know part of this story, the day Mrs. Roosevelt came to visit Jersey Homesteads." She told Pamela and Bruce, that was before we changed our town's name to Roosevelt. Everyone in Roosevelt still talks about it. But she told us it was also the day that she and Papa had a picnic with Mrs. Roosevelt in Assunpink Park. Most people in town do not know about that.

Mama told us how she and Papa put on their best casual clothes. They couldn't put on their Sunday best to go out to Assunpink. But they also couldn't put on everyday clothes to meet the wife of the President of the United States.
Pamela asked about Mrs. Roosevelt, and Mama told her that Mrs. Roosevelt and her friend Miss Hickock were regular people. There was no "I'm the wife of the president," or "I'm a famous newspaper writer." None of that. The two of them rolled up in their car, got out, and introduced themselves. Mama said she was feeling kind of shy, but Mrs. Roosevelt had sparkling, shiny blue eyes and she acted like there was no where else in the world she would want to be, like there was nothing in the world that could be more important than being in Assunpink Park with Mama and Papa. And, Mrs. Roosevelt seemed a little shy herself.

But not Miss Hickock. Miss Hickock was a woman who enjoys every bit of life in its fullest. Mama said Miss Hickock and Mrs. Roosevelt were good for each other, they balanced each other out.

Mama glowed as she told us about how Mrs. Roosevelt's eyes twinkled even more brightly when she saw me. I was only three months old. Yanina I was younger than our Joy is now when I first met Mrs. Roosevelt! Mama said Mrs. Roosevelt asked if she could hold me and cooed to me the entire time that Miss Hickock got the things out of the car and they all walked to a picnic area. Mrs. Roosevelt cradled me and talked to me like we were long-lost friends.

When everyone got everything to the picnic spot, Miss Hickock spread out a blanket. As she was pulling things out of the basket she said, "We have salads." When Mama and Papa heard that the two of them couldn't help themselves, they laughed like it was the funniest joke ever. Papa was holding his side and tears were running down his cheeks he was laughing so hard. The two of them must have been laughing like two fools. Mrs. Roosevelt asked Miss Hickock, "What did you say?" Miss Hickock said, "I only said we brought salads."

They looked at each other, then they looked at Mama and Papa. Mama said she was sure they must have been wondering what they had gotten themselves into with these crazy characters.

Mama and Papa tried to collect themselves. Mama said she was sure that they were laughing because they were nervousness being there with Mrs. Roosevelt and her friend. When she took a breath and tried to stop laughing, she got the hiccups. While Mama was trying to get herself together, Papa told them the story of how their first date was over a salad. No wonder salads are so important to Mama. I suspected that there had to be more to it than Aunt Stasia's soliloquy about the meaning of the layers of salads at my birthday dinner last year.

Papa also told them about Mama going door-to-door to meet our neighbors and to find their way in town, and how their connection with the people in town started with a salad. Then Papa said all they needed was a cup of coffee to seal the deal of being friends. Miss Hickock pulled out a thermos of coffee and the four of them had another friendly laugh.
Mrs. Roosevelt said she visited the wives of government officials in the afternoons while her husband was Assistant Secretary of the Navy. Papa and Miss Hickock, who insisted they call her 'Hick,' decided that Mrs. Roosevelt and Mama could be door-to-door sales people if their current lives did not work out. Bruce said a laugh is a great way to begin a picnic and to build a friendship. Mama patted his arm and said, "A laugh and a nice salad."

After the laughing settled down, Hick unpacked the rest of the picnic basket. There were salads to beat the band. Potato salad like Mama had never tasted, made with oil and vinegar not mayonnaise. Mrs. Roosevelt said it was her cook's favorite. The cook used to called it German Potato salad, but since Germany was at war with so much of the world, she called it Hyde Park Potato Salad. Hick thought that was the funniest thing. She said "Hyde Park Potato Salad," and laughed. Mama said she and Papa did not get the joke, but they laughed along with her because you do that with friends.

There was also cole slaw and cold green bean salad too. Mama had never had cold green bean salad, but she said it was tasty.

Mama said that anything Mrs. Roosevelt and Hick brought, they would have enjoyed. They brought fried chicken that melted in your mouth. And the best brownies Mama had ever eaten, all moist and fudgie. As Mama ate her first one (she said she had two right there and two more that night) she could taste something a little different. Hick watched Mama. She got this mischevious look on her face and waited. Mama tasted more thoughtfully. Hick laughed, "Can't place it can you?" Mama said there was something in that brownie that gave it an extra flavor, but she couldn't put her finger on it. Hick smiled and said, "peanut butter." Mama laughed with her mouth full of brownie and said, "I'll be."

Mama laughed, "There I was laughing and talking with food in my mouth with Mrs. Roosevelt. It was so relaxed and natural. Oh, those peanut butter brownies. They were the best. Eventually I figured out how to make them like that, and now they are Joan's favorite desert."

Mrs. Roosevelt hardly ate much at all, but she enjoyed what she ate. Hick kept up with Papa bite for bite and she enjoyed every bite.

What a picnic that must have been.

Mama said the time flew by, and all too soon, Hick was reminding Mrs. Roosevelt they had to be moving along if they were going to get to Washington on time. As they gathered up all the picnic things Mrs. Roosevelt insisted that Mama and Papa take the basket and the remaining food to our house as a little something to remember the day. Mama said she promised to put the picnic basket to good use. And Mama is a woman of her word. Yanina that is the basket we still use for picnics at the park.

Mrs. Roosevelt said she and Hick would stop by the factory to say hello. They would go by the school to see our mural, then to the store to visit with people. That would give Mama and Papa time to drop off the picnic things at our house and casually walk to the store, so they could 'meet' her and Hick there. That way they could be part of the buzz in town about meeting her.

And that is what they did. Mama and Papa and I walked home, dropped off our new picnic things, and set off to the store. They didn't even bother to put the food away. Papa said that would take too long, and he wanted to get to the store before Mrs. Roosevelt and Hick got there, so they could look casual. Papa wanted to get some ice cream. (He did love his Jersey Maid ice cream.) Then they could get all excited with everyone else when Mrs. Roosevelt and Hick walked into the store.

Yanina, we know the stories about this next part. Everyone got crazy excited. Mrs. Roosevelt and Miss Hickock were as cordial as could be. They said hello to everyone, and asked people what President Roosevelt could do to help them, what they needed for their lives to be better. Remember how Zayde talked about when Hick noticed Brony eating his peach ice cream cone, and she had to try some too. And then she and Mrs. Roosevelt were on their way.

Yanina, I have met Mrs. Roosevelt. But I don't remember it because I was so young. But I want to meet her again, to thank her for those letters to Mama. I will write to her and thank her, but I would so love to meet her and thank her in person.

Yanina, you should have seen Mama telling that story. She lit up as she remembered that picnic. Where does she keep that version of herself? She must have been in her early 20s then. If she is so different now, I wonder what we will be like when we are her age. I wonder how being a single mother will change me?

Anyway, Columbia accepted Pamela into the Graduate School of Arts and Science, so we can share my apartment. She will move in next week, and will keep the apartment for the summer. She is totally on cloud nine about getting into Columbia. It was her first choice. Her feet have not touched the floor since she got the letter. Bruce only has one more semester at Columbia, because he took extra courses every semester to graduate early. Lucky dog. He said something about his sister applying to Columbia's graduate school and winked at Pamela—interesting.

Bruce is consumed with working out a plan to spend a year in an ashram in India once he graduates. He read that *Autobiography of a Yogi* book, and now all he talks about is Hindu stuff. There are so many gods and goddesses! And Bruce is determined to go to India and find each one of them.

Mama's story makes me want to meet Mrs. Roosevelt all the more. Her life is so full of meaning and purpose.

I guess I've got to be patient with myself, and give myself a little more time to figure out what I will do after I graduate, in addition to being a mother to Joy, obviously. Bruce says Joy and I should go to India with him. Why would he even say that?

You asked me about Bubba. I spent a few hours with her yesterday. She is not the same since she lost Zayde. She says she is getting along. But her eyes have no light in them, no sparkle. She does what needs to be done, but only that.

Yesterday was Thursday, and she was out there with everyone else sweeping her sidewalks and the curb in front of her house. But she looks wilted, like a cabbage someone forgot in the back of the refrigerator.

What's your tale, Nightingale? Tell me what you hear from those UN people?

Always,

Joan

Joan to Yanina

July 10, 1962

Dear Yanina,

Bruce and Pamela were here when I got your letter answering our question about housing. We were all laughing as we read about you and Sadie laughing. I guess laughter is contagious, even across the Mediterranean Sea and the Atlantic Ocean.

After we stopped laughing, and we realized that the answer to our question is that Israel's Defense Forces are coed, but not that coed. The women have their units and housing; and the men theirs. We were hoping for something more avant garde. This week Pamela wants everything to be avant garde.

We read the rest of your letter and tried to picture Kasefet. The housing arrangements sound complicated. Singles rooms and couple's rooms, which are small apartments; a babies' nursery and children's dorms like at boarding schools; decisions all made by a committee. How does anything get done? Yet, your kibbutz is a collective that works. When Roosevelt was Jersey Homesteads, it was a collective that never quite worked.
In Roosevelt, our homes are right next to each other, one for each family, but you are right, the living arrangements are all unique. Bubba and Zayde each have their own room, and you and Avraham shared a bedroom. Bubba and Zayde loved each other deeply, even though it would mortify them if someone noticed it, but they each had separate bedrooms.

Mama and Aunt Stasia are not married, but they share a bedroom. I have my own bedroom, which I now share with Joy. And we have a whole other room devoted to books and Aunt Stasia's meditation space. People just live the way they live.

Bubba and Zayde were always a little formal and formidable with other people, but your home was filled with emotion. Mama and Aunt Stasia are more relaxed and informal, but everyone in our house lives in their heads. I guess everybody lives as they live.

We all just had some Jersey Maid ice cream on our way to the post office, so Bruce is delighted that you have your Strauss ice cream.

And I can hear Joy fussing. I want to get her before Mama or Aunt Stasia. More later.

Always,

Joan

Telegram: Eva Zatańczy to Yanina
Telegram: Roosevelt, NJ to Kasefet, Israel

July 19, 1962

To: Yanina Kominiarski
From: Eva Zatańczy

Our Joy died in her sleep on July 15. We buried her yesterday. Joan is inconsolable. Please write.

Yanina to Joan

20 July 1962

Dear Joan,

Oh Joan, I am heartbroken with you; I am grieving with you. Joy filled your life, your world with love, with light, with meaning. And now she is gone. Oh, Joan, my soul-sister, I ache to be there with you, to sit side by side and weep together. Joan, I know you are devastated.

Joan, we have a saying here in Kasefet, "In a long life there will be *tsoris*." You have had enough anguish and suffering in this year for a lifetime. Remember how Aunt Stasia used to say, "If you love, you will grieve"? We would roll our eyes and snicker. But now is a time to grieve. Give yourself time and space. Give your broken heart space to cry. Cry for as long as you need. Give yourself time to cry your heart out.

Joan, you have been through so much this past year, and you always kept going. Give yourself time to pause. Like Mrs. Roosevelt says, find a place of solace where you can mourn and grieve. Healing is a slow process, but it will happen for you. There is another shore beyond these shoals of grief. In time you will find your way beyond those shoals.

With hope for a better tomorrow, *mortgaged*, I am missing you,

Yanina

From Mrs. Roosevelt to Joan

July 22, 1962

Dear Joan,

I just learned of the death of your dear Joy. You have my deepest, heartfelt condolences. Death and loss may be inevitable in our world, but the loss of one's child is the most grievous of all losses.

I know your mother and Aunt Stasia will do all they can to help you. However my experience has taught me that each of us must navigate the path of grieving in our own way. Death creates an emptiness, a listlessness, a vacuum. Each of us must learn to live with that emptiness, that listlessness, that vacuum, in our own particular way. Each of us experiences and lives with loss in our lives uniquely, even as we share the common experience of death.

I still remember my aunt telling me that my father had died. I was not eleven years old. I nearly cried myself to sleep. But before I fell asleep, I created my own little world where my Papa and I could still be together. In my make-believe world, I relived all the best times I had with my Papa. I lived out all the promises my Papa made to me of the things we were going to do together. I lived out all of my dreams and hopes for things we might have done.

Joan, to this day, there are moments when the events that accost me are more than I can bear and I take solace in my land of day dreams, in a "well put together unreality" to borrow the words of Mr. Mark Twain. There I can engage with the foibles, frailties and follies of human nature in manageable iterations. There I can take refuge with lost family and friends, and even heroines who I know only through books and stories. A place of sanctuary and solace can be a comfort, as long as your escape is only a temporary resting place.

Joan, solace and strength are two things I would send to you in this letter. You may not have a home for them in your heart for some time, but in time, I hope you will find a place for them. To this day, when I search for solace and strength, I look to the letters that my Papa wrote me. His unwavering belief in me has helped me to find my strength in my moments of doubt. He would encourage me to strengthen my resolve to do good in the world while doing my personal best to build my discipline, to learn from the lessons in school and in life, and to understand that the frustrations I encountered could serve an agenda for lessons to be learned.

More than anything, in his letters, my father always told me how much he loved me and how much he believed in me. To this day those sentiments hold a special place in my heart. My father encouraged me to be noble, brave, studious, religious, loving, and good. My father always saw the best in me and I have worked hard to live up to his belief in me.

Joan, through your mother's letters to me about you, I see you emerging as a woman with a good heart, a delightful exuberance, and a wonderful curiosity. I know the day will come when you will find your place in this world as a fine and noble woman of strong purpose.

The loss of someone we love is a hard burden to bear. The pain of their absence in our lives is heart breaking, most especially when you have lost your child. Joan, remember a broken heart can become an open heart. It can give us a special tenderness for those whose lives are awash with grief and suffering. If we learn to live with our heart open to others, then we can act with compassion and resolve to ease the burdens of others.

Dear Joan, strive to keep your heart open to love, to always do your best, to learn each day. Dedicate yourself to helping others and you will help yourself as well.

Fondly,

Mrs. Roosevelt

Joan to Yanina

August 22, 1962

Dear Yanina,

My sweet, precious Joy is gone. I have lost my joy.
Yanina, babies can sleep on their back, babies can sleep on their side, but babies should never sleep on their stomach because sleeping on their stomach makes them more susceptible to Sudden Infant Death Syndrome. SIDS is what doctors call it when a healthy baby dies in her sleep. It's a fancy way of saying the baby stopped breathing, and the doctors doesn't know why.

One nurse told me the babies of mothers who smoke or drink alcohol or use drugs are more susceptible to SIDS. I felt like she knew Smyth got me drunk the night we conceived Joy, like she knew Pamela, Bruce and I smoked marijuana before Joy was born.

What did I do to my Joy? I overheard an intern saying babies with blankets or pajamas that are too warm are more susceptible. My doctor told me that stomach sleeping is most associated with SIDS.

Joy was just learning to turn herself over. On July 14, I put her to sleep on her side, with the pillow behind her, like we had been doing. I looked at her before I went to sleep and she was fine. Something woke me up around 3 in the morning. I sat up in bed for no reason. I went over to check on her, and my sweet precious Joy was lying on her stomach. I bent down to roll her over. I knew something was not right. I picked her up to see what was going on, and she wasn't breathing.

Yanina, I lost my breath. I couldn't speak. I screamed. Mama and Aunt Stasia came running. Aunt Stasia took one look at Joy and tried to give her mouth to mouth resuscitation. Sometimes it's good she's a nurse. But not that night. That night nothing was good.

Zayde died, and we grieved him, I grieved but I could see that death at the end of a long life well lived is inevitable, is natural. But there is nothing inevitable or natural about the death of a baby, of my baby.

My Joy is gone. I am empty and in a fog. I am drowning in an ocean of fog. I can't move. I can't breathe. I can't think.

All I can do is cry. I should never have had that wine with Smyth. I should never have smoked that marijuana with Pamela and Bruce. There are so many things I never should have done. It all seemed like a good idea at the time.

Mama was right. Nothing good ever comes from being a free spirit. I was better off being focused and disciplined.

My sweet, sweet Joy was not even 5 months old. She was my purpose, the meaning of my life and now she is gone.

Aunt Stasia said I should write to you. So I did. But now what do I do?

Joan

# *Part V*
# *Fall Semester 1962*

Joan to Yanina

September 10, 1962

Dear Yanina,

Classes have started and I still wake up each morning listening for Joy's cry. Then I remember, and I cry. It is nearly two months since I found my Joy lying there. Every morning I cry myself awake. Mama and Aunt Stasia took care of her every day. I can't even imagine how they are feeling. Mama doesn't talk, not about anything. Aunt Stasia meditates, just siting. The house is so quiet. I couldn't wait to get out of there.
This past year there were times my heart was broken. But this, losing Joy, my heart is demolished. I wake up and my chest is an empty, aching crater. I remember Joy's sweet smiling face; the scent of her hair after her bath. I can't breathe. I remember Aunt Stasia telling me to breathe—inhale, exhale, repeat as necessary.

Somehow remembering that stupid phrase, "repeat as necessary" calls me back to myself. Not the self I was. Not the Joan Zatańczy who graduated from Roosevelt Public School, who left Roosevelt to go the big city and attend Barnard College, who turned 21 a lifetime ago. That Joan has been destroyed. Aunt Stasia says a phoenix will grow in the vacuum where my heart used to be. I can't imagine it.

KarenMarie came to visit last week. She tried to tell me that Joy's death is not my fault. She said the nurse never should have said those things to me; there is no harm in one glass of wine, getting a little drunk once, smoking marijuana once. KarenMarie told me that one of her sisters is a nurse, and her sister told her they really don't know what causes SIDS. She kept telling me that Joy's death is not my fault. But the more she said it, the worse I felt. Why is everyone so eager to fix this, to fix me?

I am broken. Just let me be.

Since Joy's funeral Bruce and Pamela have come to Roosevelt a lot. They have been with me through all of this. They sat with me and all I did was cry. I keep thinking, "Why did she have to die? What did I do wrong?" I guess I must have been saying that out loud too, because Bruce said that if I was in India I could call on the Devi Parvati, the great Mother, to help me. Bruce and India and his Hindu gods and goddesses.

He's cute, but sometimes he can be a little too obsessed with all of that. Still, when Bruce talks about going to the Ashram and finding Mother Teresa, there are days I am tempted to go with him.

Bruce told me he is reading *Farewell to Arms* by Ernest Hemingway, and there is a line in the book, "The world will break you. Then you become strong in the broken places." I told Bruce that not a shred of me has not been broken this past year. He gave me a hug and told me that not a shred of me will not be strong. He still calls me Joan of Roosevelt. To tell you the truth, I feel more in tune with Marilyn Monroe, "I am good, but not an angel. I do sin, but I am not the devil. I am just a small girl in a big world trying to find someone to love."

She died from an overdose a few days ago. But no, I am not that in tune with her. Things are rough for me now, but I don't understand how she could throw everything away. I am feeling like a small girl in a big world, but I keep remembering Aunt Stasia's phoenix and hoping I will find a way out of the ashes of this nightmare.

Now that I am back at Barnard, Bruce is trying hard to get me back into college life. He gave me a copy of last week's issue of the Barnard Bulletin, saying it would cheer me up. There was an article about Barnard's Dress Code. Barnard girls are not allowed to wear slacks or Bermuda shorts on Columbia's campus. If we wear Bermuda shorts on Barnard's campus they can't be more than 2 inches above the knee, they can't be brightly colored, and they must fit properly (meaning not too tight). And we are only allowed to sunbathe on the roofs of Helen Reid and Barnard Halls.

Who has time to make up those rules? Pamela read the piece and said she can't decide if the dress code is funny or infuriating. Mostly, I don't care. But it was nice that Bruce tried.

I just reread a letter Mrs. Roosevelt wrote about a trip she took to Japan. I'm sending you that one. She met these old ladies, the Shibokusa mothers. They lost so much, and they still managed to laugh. I wonder if I will ever laugh again.
Yanina, I can only say this to you. I am starting to wonder what kind of person I am. As the days go by, as I cry my eyes dry, I am realizing that under the grief, under the desolation, under all of that, is something like relief. What is wrong with me? I love my Joy. I am grief stricken for her. How can even a part of me be relieved that she is gone and I won't have as many struggles to face, that I won't have to figure out how to be a single mother?

Yesterday I caught myself thinking I am relieved that I didn't risk getting kicked out of school to force Smyth pay child support. I would have been on hold in the cold, and he would have been home free. How can I have those feelings? What is wrong with me!

Enough about me. What's your tale, Nightingale? How are things with you in Kasefet? Have you heard from the UNRWA yet? I worry about you going into the Gaza. Please be careful. Please be safe.

Always,

Joan

ER to Eva

July 18, 1953

Dear Eva,

I am recently returned from an extended trip to Japan where I traveled with my secretary, Miss Maureen Corr, and my daughter-in-law Mrs. Elliott Roosevelt. Both women are wonderful traveling companions. We all were pleasant company to each other for our five weeks in a profoundly different culture. In Japan there were endless meetings with government ministers, professors, students, even Emperor Hirohito and his wife. Those are commitments I must fulfill as the widow of a past president and as a former United States representative to the United Nations. But the parts of my travels that I most welcome are the opportunities to talk with the people of the country I am visiting.

One of the most interesting experiences I had was when we reviewed the American military base at the foot of Mount Fuji and where we also spoke with a group of women who call themselves the Shibokusa Mothers Committee. Since the seventeenth century families have lived at the base of Mount Fuji, farming vegetables and raising silkworms. But at the beginning of World War II, the government disbursed the farming community to make way for a military base. After the war, when our military took over the base, prostitution expanded and women in the area lost even more of their status and stature.

But the Shibokusa Mothers are not to be toyed with. They have a strong sense of community, a clear sense of righteousness, and a deep and abiding sense of humor. As I spoke with the women whose families had long lived at the base of Mount Fuji, I saw how community, righteousness, and humor are resources that produce great resilience and grit.

When I met with the Shibokusa Mothers, I was interested in talking with them about the attitudes of young people towards their elders, of elders towards young people, and about problems related to prostitution and babies born of mixed ethnicities.

But I don't always get what I want.

The Shibokusa Mothers are strong in body and mind. Most of the women I met with were in their fifties and sixties and they wanted to discuss the use of the atomic bomb and putting an end to all wars. I am used to setting my own agenda, or being told ahead of time, often by the State Department, what the agenda will be. But these women simply ignored the planned agenda and discussed the topics on their minds.

I am appalled by the effects of the atomic bomb, but I tried to explain the urgent reasons the United States saw for using the bomb to end the war as quickly as possible. But these women were intransigent in their assertion that there is never an adequate justification for using atomic bombs. They were also intransigent in their insistence that the land at the foot of Mount Fuji is their ancestral farmland and should be returned to them.

The women want the military base and the soldiers on it to leave and the land to be returned to farming. They are persistent and creative in their approach to disrupting the activities of the base and regaining their land.

I found it interesting to see how two groups in such close proximity can have wildly divergent perspectives on events and on each other. When I spoke with some soldiers, I learned that they are sharply aware of the women who camp around the base. They find them bothersome and irritating. The officers told me how the women dress in baggy pants and wide straw hats. They sneak around building smoky fires and flying kites to foul up the artillery tests. At times the women lay in the road so trucks can't pass in or out of the base. At other times the women sit around and sing or they stand and point at the men in their uniforms, laughing so that the men felt mocked.

When I talked with the women, they told me humor was their most powerful weapon. They are intentional in nurturing their ability to find humor everywhere. I asked them if the police ever came to move them away from the military base. The women laughed (they laughed a lot) and said the police often move them away and sometimes arrest them. When the police question the Shibokusa Mothers, they keep their silence. When asked their names, the women say, "I am old and I don't remember anymore. I don't remember when I was born or what my name is." And they laugh. The Shibokusa Mothers may be easy to arrest, but they are a lot of trouble to deal with once they are arrested. They have nothing to lose, so nothing threatens them.

As I talked with these women, they impressed me with their down-to-earth audacity, authenticity, and ingenuity. I have never met a group of people who more ebulliently exuded joy. Even in the middle of their struggle, they find joy in their effort.

My translator told me it has to do with something called wabi sabi. That is something your Stasia might know from her Buddhism? It has to do with change as a constant, and the persistent pervasiveness of imperfection. The Shibokusa Mothers may tell the police they do not remember their names or when they were born, but they remember Hiroshima and Nagasaki. They remember to disrupt the actions from the military base at the foot of Mount Fuji. Their conviction that violence is wrong is unshakeable. These women are committed to peace; they invite and encourage others to join that commitment, each in her unique way.

It is not within me to disrupt military activities in the clandestine ways these women are doing, but I am heartened by the strength of their commitment to peace. They inspire me to continue working for peace and human rights. We can each find our way to do that work. Indeed, we each must seek ways to encourage and support each other as we work together, in our unique ways, toward the same grand goal.

The Shibokusa Mothers remind me of the importance of humor and of taking yourself lightly. As my Aunt Bamie was fond of saying "Angels fly because they take themselves so lightly." I think the Shibokusa Mothers would agree with her.

Dear Eva, it was quite a journey, this trip to Japan. As I settle in at home, the most ardent desire of my heart is that there be peace on earth. May we all do one thing each day to bring more peace and laughter into our world.

With love, your affectionate friend,

Eleanor

Joan to Yanina

September 28, 1962

Dear Yanina,

Classes are in full swing here at Barnard, but who cares. Mrs. Roosevelt had some hard times. Those people in Japan—the Shibokusa Mothers, and the people around Hiroshima—they had some hard times (I'm sending you her letter about her second trip to Japan when she went to Hiroshima). Even Mama and Aunt Stasia had some hard times. I read the bag letters from Mrs. Roosevelt, and it seems like they set those hard times behind them, turned a corner, and opened the door to new chapters in their lives. I keep trying, but I'm tired, too tired to lift my hand to open a door. Honestly, I don't care enough to try.

People try to be nice. They keep asking me about my baby. They don't know her name or even if the baby was a boy or a girl. All I hear is "Hi Joan, how's the baby?" What am I supposed to say, "My baby is not so great, she died." I can't say that. I am tired of dancing around to finesse an answer to their dumb, meaningless greeting. I hope the word spreads soon. Lord knows, gossip spreads around here like kudzu in Carolina (convocation this semester was "Protecting Our Environment").

I wish I could graduate and get out of here. But I can't go back home to Roosevelt. The house reminds me of Joy. It must be hard for Mama and Aunt Stasia to be there all the time. They were more mothers to her than I was. I know they are hurting too. But I can't go back there. Maybe I will stay in New York.

I am sad all the time. I sit in the apartment and stare. Pamela and Bruce have been great. But I worry they will get sick of my mopping around. I worry Pamela will want to move out of the apartment and she just moved in three months ago. Pamela is elated to be starting grad school. Bruce is making plans to go to that Ashram in Calcutta. And I am a downer.

But every night before supper, Bruce opens a bottle of wine and the three of us sit and talk. They let me cry for a while, then Pamela says, "OK, now let's take a deep breath, raise our spirits to the spirit of Joy." We toast the life that might have been, that never will be. And we move on. Well, they move on and I sit there. When Bruce leaves for the night, he hugs me and says, "Don't let the sun catch you crying." It has become our ritual. Last night Bruce said, "Come to India with me. Get away from all of this." Maybe I should go with him. Maybe things would be different in India.

How do I live with a heart ripped into shreds? Aunt Stasia says this is the kind of thing you don't figure out, you just keep living. One breath, one step at a time, you live through today into tomorrow. She also says "Life at its best is joyful participation in a world of sorrows." I guess she's right. But sometimes she is too Buddhist. I don't like the idea of living in a world of sorrows. Why can't I live in a world of joy with my Joy? Instead I am in my world of sorrows; one breath, one step, one sip of wine at a time, I keep doing what I need to do.

I had four goals. I wanted to finish my thesis, and that is done. I wanted to graduate from Barnard, one more semester and that will be done.

I wanted to meet Mrs. Roosevelt and tell her how much her letters have meant to me, and how important that sack of letters has been to me, but I can't figure out how to accomplish that. And I wanted to figure out the meaning of life, of my life. I found that meaning in Joy, in loving Joy. But she died, and my sense of meaning and purpose died with her. I was so pretentious, I wanted to do something big and important; but reality ripped that dream out of my heart. Now I feel absurd for wanting so much. I feel sad and absurd. I've given up my quest for the grand meaning of life. At least Dr. Fredrick's course taught me one thing: Camus was right, it is absurd to yearn for significance when we are caught in an infinite, cold universe.

Mrs. Roosevelt and her letters are the one constant in my pitiful life. These days I keep rereading the letter about her second trip to Japan. She visited with children from Hiroshima who were dying from leukemia they got from radiation poisoning. They were folding paper cranes for peace. Maybe I should start folding origami cranes. It worked for those kids in Hiroshima. One thousand cranes—it would give me something to do.

So, what's your tale, Nightingale? What is the news from Kasefet kibbutz?

Always,

Joan

ER to Eva

September 26, 1955

Dear Eva,

I have recently returned to Hyde Park following my second trip to Japan. I was interested in seeing for myself how the women of Japan were faring ten years after the war. My wonderful secretary Maureen Corr, my dear friend Trude Lash, and I set out on a trip to explore the current state of conditions in Japan. For me, one of the most profound experiences of the trip was our journey to Hiroshima where the United States dropped the first atomic bomb.
As we traveled throughout the city, I learned about Hiroshima's history. In the 1860s during the Meiji Restoration, Hiroshima City was redeveloped as the capital of the Hiroshima Prefecture. Built on a delta, surrounded by sea, rivers, and mountains, and graced by large trees, the city housed schools and businesses and thriving commercial districts.

By the latter half of the 1930s industries in the city converted to military plants and the harbor took on a military ambience. The Kure naval base was located there. Since the United States dropped the atomic bomb on it, Hiroshima has begun to recreate itself as "Peace City Hiroshima."

In the United States, we believed using an atomic bomb was necessary to end the war with Japan as quickly as possible. We believed this would save the lives of thousands of our boys, and would keep Russia from taking control of Japan when it surrendered. When I visited Japan, I wanted to learn their beliefs regarding the ending of the war and of the role of the atomic bombings. I will simply say their perspective is starkly different from that held in America.

We visited the Genbaku Dome in an area designated to become a Peace Memorial. I learned that Genbaku means atomic bomb in Japanese. The dome is near the center of where our atomic bomb exploded on August 6, 1945. The dome rises as a skeleton in the detritus of the Hiroshima Prefectural Industrial Promotional Hall surrounding it. To see the destructive power of the bomb was overwhelming. It is fitting that the site of the first atomic bombing should become a memorial to the urgent need for world peace.

While we were visiting the area that will be Hiroshima Peace Park area, I learned of plans to create a Children's Peace Monument with a statue dedicated to the memory of the children who died as a result of the bombing. In the years since the atomic bomb, there has been an explosion of leukemia among children who were in the vicinity of Hiroshima and Nagasaki. By the time of my visit it was clear that radiation exposure caused the leukemia.

We visited a hospital in Hiroshima where I met some children with leukemia. To see so many children in the hospital still suffering the effects of the atomic bomb was heart breaking. But the children's spirits were undaunted, I saw a quiet joy in their eyes as they practiced origami, the Japanese art of paper folding. They were folding paper cranes. Our interpreter recounted an ancient Japanese legend which says that anyone who folds one thousand paper cranes will be granted a wish. She said the children were folding paper cranes to be cured of leukemia. I am not sure if the imminent loss of young, innocent lives or their unrequited hope saddened me more.

As I was leaving the hospital, one girl took my hand and asked the interpreter to tell me not to be sad for them. She said they knew they were dying; they were not folding the cranes to be cured, but for an end to bombings, an end to war, and for peace in the world. She asked the interpreter to tell me, "This is our cry. This is our prayer. Peace in our world." I will confess those words brought tears to my eyes. I pray her prayer will be answered.

I have added those words to the devotion I say each night as I take to my bed:

*Our Father, who has set a restlessness in our hearts and made us all seekers after that which we can never fully find, forbid us to be satisfied with what we make of life. Draw us from base content and set our eyes on far-off goals. Keep us at tasks too hard for us that we may be driven to Thee for strength.*

*Deliver us from fretfulness and self-pitying; make us sure of the good we cannot see, of the hidden good in the world. Open our eyes to the simple beauty all around us and our hearts to the loveliness men hide from us because we do not understand them. Save us from ourselves and show us a vision of a world made new. Dear Father, this is my cri de coeur, the cry from my heart. This is my prayer. May there be peace in our world.*

Eva, it is ever clearer to me that talking about peace is not enough. One must believe in it. But, believing in peace is also not enough. One must work at it. My Dear Eva, I am convinced that if we are to prevent another Hiroshima, we must all commit ourselves to working for peace in our world, each of us in our way, using our particular skills and abilities the best we can. And as I write those words to you, I find myself thinking about your most recent letter to me. Indeed peace is precarious, even in the most loving of homes.

I am sorry to hear of the discord between you and Anastasia. Your concerns regarding Joan's desire to attend Barnard and to live in New York City are understandable. Anastasia's inclination to support Joan's dream is also understandable. Barnard's reputation as an educational institution for young women is unparalleled. Eva, you both have Joan's best interests at heart. I trust you will both open your hearts to each other, to listen to each other's fears and hopes, and to regain peace in your home.

With love, your affectionate friend,

Eleanor

Joan to Yanina

October 21, 1962

Dear Yanina,

It is the end of October. One hundred days; two thousand four hundred hours; one hundred forty-four thousand minutes since Joy died. And I miss her every minute, every second. I wake up crying, and I wonder if I will be able to get dressed, if I will be able to get myself out of the apartment. Somehow, I go to classes and do assignments. I go through the motions.

And, yes, I do remember Aunt Stasia's story about the lady who was overwhelmed with grief because her infant died. Aunt Stasia and her Buddha stories. Of course the Buddha promised to cure the lady's suffering, and of course there was a condition—bring him a mustard seed from a family who had not lost a loved one to death. I remember the first time Aunt Stasia told us that story. It sounded like such a simple task. Aunt Stasia let us think for a minute. Then she named all the families the grieving mother visited. Aunt Stasia had to be making those names up. Finally you burst out, "Isn't there any family in that entire village that had not been touched by death?" I can see Aunt Stasia smiling as she said, "not one."

Finally we all, you and I, and the grieving mother, we all realized that if we love we will grieve. If we live, we will die. But, oh Yanina, I didn't expect my Joy to die before she even had a chance to live.

I wake up every morning grieving. Now after I cry for a while, I practice some of Aunt Stasia's breathing meditation. It is ironic that my Joy died because she stopped breathing, and I am learning to live again by focusing on my breath. I remind myself of the grieving mother story, and I do what I need to do to get through the day.

Joan

Joan to Yanina

November 1, 1962

Dear Yanina,

Today started like every other day, but then. . . then I remember there was a field trip for Dr. Cobbe's Social Welfare: Roots and Wings course. I almost didn't go, but she is a stickler about assignments and special projects, and after all she did to help me last year, I knew I had to show up. We were going to meet a social worker at Columbia-Presbyterian Hospital and then visit the Henry Street Settlement.

When we got to the hospital Hilda Corrigan, the head of social services, met us and took us to a conference room where we all sat around this immense, impressive wooden table. It smelled important in that room, like lemon wax and new shoes. I sat taller in my leather chair. Yanina, it's strange, but something shifted in me as I breathed the smells in that room. I could smell hope in the lemon wax and leather.

Mrs. Corrigan talked about the history of the hospital and when social workers started to work there. She talked about what social workers did in the hospital, discharge planning, and working with the doctors and nurses to be sure patients had a safe place to return to when they left the hospital. She caught my attention when she said our tour would be limited because Mrs. Eleanor Roosevelt was a patient on the fifth floor and access to that floor was restricted.

Mrs. Roosevelt in the hospital, right there, in that hospital. I read that Mrs. Roosevelt had been sick, but she was right there where I was.

We broke up into small groups for our tours, with a social worker leading each group. I pulled Bruce aside and told him to cover for me. You know I had to get to the fifth floor to see Mrs. Roosevelt. She was so close. I had to see her. I slipped away from the group, found my way to the elevators and pushed the button for the fifth floor. It was easy.

I got off the elevator and discovered that the fifth floor was huge, and there were security guards checking badges and ID cards. It would not be so easy.

I ducked into the shadows to get my bearings and to get a sense of what was going on around me. Then I saw a small group of professional looking people deep in conversation, walking down the hall. I moved out from my corner and tried to blend in with them. I guess I was not as smooth as I thought, because a lady in the group looked at me and asked, "Can I help you, dear?" She was wearing a visitor name tag, and my eyes nearly burst out of my head when I saw her name, "Maureen Corr." I swallowed hard, took a deep breath and asked her, "Aren't you Mrs. Roosevelt's secretary?"
"I am." she said, "How did you know? You don't look like a newspaper reporter. Who are you, dear? And, what are you doing on this floor?"

I blathered about being Joan Zatańczy and Mrs. Roosevelt writing letters to my Mama for twenty years and being in the hospital with my class from Barnard College, and hearing that Mrs. Roosevelt was here, and wanting to thank her for the condolence letter she wrote to me when my Joy died, for all she has done to inspire me. I took a breath. Ms. Corr was looking at me with a sad look, the kind adults get when they want to be nice but bad news is coming.

"Joan, I typed many of Mrs. Roosevelt's letters to your mother." She said she knew Mrs. Roosevelt was fond of Mama and me, but Mrs. Roosevelt was seriously ill, too ill for visitors.

I wept as she talked. I could feel the tears on my cheeks, onion cutting tears, those quiet, sad tears that leak out of your eyes without your even knowing.

Ms. Corr softened, and said that there wouldn't be any harm in having a look through the door, I could at least see Mrs. Roosevelt. Then she put her arm though mine, and we walked down the hall to Mrs. Roosevelt's room, like we belonged there, because one of us actually did belong there. When we got to the room Mrs. Roosevelt was sleeping.

I stood insider her door, at the foot of her bed, it was amazing to see her, to be that close to her. It is totally cliché, but my heart was all a flutter, thundering in my chest. I was basking in the moment, letting myself relish seeing Mrs. Roosevelt, being close enough to see her. I was overjoyed to be seeing her, but sad that she was so ill.

Like a prayer, I said, "Thank you, Mrs. Roosevelt. Thank you for everything." At that moment, the hospital public address system blared out, "Joan Zatańczy, please return to the social services office on the main floor. Your school van will leave in ten minutes. Joan Zatańczy return to the social services office on the main floor immediately."

My face must have turned apple red. I was embarrassed and caught. Mrs. Roosevelt opened her eyes, she looked around and said, "Joan?" She recognized my name. Mrs. Roosevelt and I looked at each other, and I said, "Mrs. Roosevelt, I'm here. It's me, Joan." She whispered, "Joan."

I blurted out, "Mrs. Roosevelt, thank you. You are amazing. You have changed my life. Thank you. Thank you so much."

She smiled, and pointed to the chair by her bed and said, "Sit for a moment. Hand me that cup of water, will you please?"

She took a sip of then water, and she said, "Joan, you have been through some hard times. When I lost Franklin Junior, I grieved mightily for a time. Then I gathered my resolve and put myself back to work. Joan, gather your resolve, take up your life's work.

"I have found that women are like tea bags, you can't tell how strong we are until we are in hot water. Joan, I expect that this past year you felt you were drowning in hot water. You are grieving for your Joy. Let your grief open your heart to the suffering of others. Let your grief open the door to helping others who are struggling to preserve their dignity, who are fighting for their human rights. Human dignity and rights are lofty ideals. But they are to be found and protected in the day-to-day world of each person, in small places close to home. Like the beautiful lotus flower, justice and opportunity must set their roots in the mud of day-to-day life. Dignity resides in small things, in small places close to home. Joan, let your grief help you keep your conscience tender. A tender conscience is the best guide to strengthening human dignity. Joan, . . ."

Then she closed her eyes and drifted back to sleep. Ms. Corr reminded me that the van would be leaving. She walked me to the elevator. I floated all the way to the first floor. Yanina, as I think about what Mrs. Roosevelt said, I know what I will do with my life. I will work for women's human rights. That is a goal larger than myself. I will gather my resolve to work for women's human rights with my head, with my heart and with my hands.

I was still floating and glowing when I got down to the social services office. I apologized to Dr. Cobbe for getting separated from the other students. I told her that when we got here, I realized I had a friend in the hospital and I thought I could pop in and say hello, but I got lost. That appeased Dr. Cobbe, but Bruce didn't believe a word of what I said, I could see it in his eyes. I told him we would talk more later.

Before Bruce could ask me anything else we were being herded onto the school van and on our way to the Henry Street Settlement House. I was in a daze as we walked around the Settlement House.

I kept picturing Mrs. Roosevelt in her hospital bed. At one point I remembered that letter Mrs. Roosevelt wrote to me about her dinner at Lillian Wald's house in Connecticut. The woman who was taking us around asked if there were any questions. I asked her if Lillian Wald and Jane Addams knew each other. She didn't know if they ever met, but she was sure that they knew of each other's work. I wanted to say they had dinner together at least once, but I could see Dr. Cobbe looking at her watch, so I didn't say anything else. There were a few more questions from other kids in the class and then we were in the van heading back to Barnard.

What a most amazing, bittersweet day. I saw Mrs. Roosevelt. I got to say thank you to her. But, my thank you to Mrs. Roosevelt was also my goodbye to her.

Yanina, hope is on the horizon. To work for women and human rights, that holds hope. I can smell it, it smells like lemon wax and leather, hope is in small things close to home.

Always,

Joan

Joan to Yanina

November 15, 1962

Dear Yanina,

Mrs. Roosevelt died on November 7, in her apartment in New York City. At least she got to go home.

I wanted to go to her funeral today, but Mama said they would restrict it to family and official dignitaries. Mama said if she knew Mrs. Roosevelt at all (and after twenty years of being pen pals, Mama said she knew her well) she was sure Mrs. Roosevelt would want me to stay at Barnard and keep up with my classes and school work. Then Mama reminded me I had a paper due for Dr. Cobbe's Roots and Wings class. She's right. My paper is supposed to be about someone we thought had made a significant contribution to the foundations of social welfare. I wanted to write about Mrs. Roosevelt, but Dr. Cobbe would never let me get away with writing my thesis and my Wings paper about the same person.

But, even if I wasn't going to Mrs. Roosevelt's funeral, that didn't mean I wasn't going to know everything I possibly could about it. I read every newspaper I could find. And yet again Mrs. Roosevelt came through for me. While I was in Barnard's library pouring over their newspapers, I noticed an old copy of The New York Times from January 1961. Why there was a copy of the Times from a year ago laying on the library floor is beyond me, but there it was folded open to the obituary pages. Right there on top was an obituary for Emily Greene Balch, picture and all.

Remember that letter Mrs. Roosevelt wrote to Mama about her?

Emily Greene Balch died when she was 94 years old. What a life she had led. She won the Nobel Peace Prize in 1946; worked with Jane Addams to create the Women's International League for Peace and Freedom; started the Denison House Settlement; and was a social worker for the Boston Children's Aid Society. She is perfect for my Roots and Wings paper.

Since I was at the library, I figured I might as well get started on my research. They had a copy of a book she wrote called Our Slavic Fellow Citizens and one that she wrote with Jane Addams and Alice Hamilton called Women at the Hague. She was amazing. She taught at Wellesley Women's college for over twenty years. Remember how Mrs. Roosevelt wrote that when she was out on a leave to do research for her book on Slavic people, she asked for an extension of her leave and Wellesley terminated her contract? Not because she wasn't doing her job, but because she was an advocate for peace. Working for peace has its costs.

As I read about Mrs. Roosevelt's funeral, I started thinking about her being dead. I thought about her letter to me on the day I was born, and her "who are you game." That got me thinking about who Eleanor Roosevelt was. She was First Lady of the state of New York, First Lady of the United States, First Lady of the United Nations and the World. She was a great progressive reformer, a national and international politician, and a feminist. She lived through more changes in our country than I can imagine. I've read that there are people who think she was a busybody.

Well, not to me, she wasn't.

She was a pioneer in fighting for the dignity of African Americans and their rights as full human beings. But she was slow in fighting for women's suffrage, the Equal Rights Amendment and child labor laws. But she grew up with strict, up tight Victorian values, in a world that taught her men were better than women. That was a lot for her to work through.
Then, there was her family. She was a Roosevelt, and they had some nice advantages. But her Mama was harsh with her, calling her 'granny' because she thought young Eleanor acted like a little old lady. And her Mama died when Mrs. Roosevelt was only 8 years old. Her father loved her like crazy, and she loved him right back. But, he drank an awful lot of alcohol, and he died before she turned 11.

Still, to Mrs. Roosevelt, her father was a warm, gentle presence. By the time it came around to raising Mrs. Roosevelt and her brother, her Grandmother Hall was the poster child for Victorian values. Mrs. Roosevelt had it easy, but she had it tough too.

She may have been full of contradictions and paradoxes to the rest of the world, but to me she was my mother's pen pal. She bared her heart in her letters and shared her dreams of a world of peace where human rights are respected. Wouldn't it be great if someday women got to be recognized as full human beings, with dignity and full human rights?

Sometimes life is wildly unfathomable and absurd, but dedicating my life to working for women's dignity and basic human rights, that has meaning.

Yanina, as I read and reread those letters from Mrs. Roosevelt I have come to take myself more seriously. I am learning what it means to be someone who is not to be trifled with, and I can see that it is important to trust other people, and sometimes to let your free spirit fly. I know Papa's going off to war and dying was hard for Mama, but, I am going to follow Mrs. Roosevelt's advice. I am going to let me grief help me to keep my conscience tender. I am going to find a way to work to strengthening human dignity.

Mrs. Roosevelt and the other powerful women we read about in classes helped me to see how public affairs and policies play out in our back yards and kitchens. There are often larger political issues that help to create the problems we live with in our home. It's like Mrs. Roosevelt was saying about small things close to home.

And, did Mrs. Roosevelt ever open my eyes to human rights. Her letters have me following everything that's on the news more carefully. After all what does it mean to be a human being if everybody doesn't get to be a full human being with dignity and respect? But how can you have dignity if you are too poor to buy food or to afford decent housing? How can you have dignity if you can't read or write or you go to school in a building that is falling apart and you don't have any books? How can you have dignity if you are sick and can't afford a doctor? How can women have dignity if we can't control something as basic as our own reproductive life? How can babies have dignity if they don't even get to live?

I still have to figure out exactly what I will do. Mrs. Roosevelt was practical. I am more like Louisa May Alcott, "Far away, there in the sunshine, are my highest aspirations. I may not reach them, but I can look up and see their beauty, believe in them and try to follow where they lead." I remember that quote and my heart opens. I remember Mrs. Roosevelt and her work and I can envision my highest aspirations: dignity and full human rights for all women everywhere.

And then I remember Joy, and I am numb and the beauty in the world evaporates. I try to remember what Mrs. Roosevelt said about my grief keeping my conscience tender. But there are days when I just can't. There are still days when I feel like I am a raw open wound. On a good day, I can hear Aunt Stasia's voice in my head saying, "Inhale, exhale. Repeat as necessary. One foot in front of the other. Graduate. Then see what comes next." I guess she is right.

The smell of lemon wax and leather helps me to stay grounded. Inhale, exhale, spray Pledge on something to keep lemon wax in the air. Our apartment has never been so clean. But Pamela put her foot down when she caught me starting to spray Pledge on the floors.

Sixty three more days until graduation, until I can put this all behind me and start the next chapter in my life, sixty three more days until I can start to work for women's human rights.

Always,

Joan

Joan to Yanina

December 12, 1962

Dear Yanina,

Yanina, a couple weeks ago I was in Roosevelt for Thanksgiving. Being in at home Roosevelt still crushes me. My heart still shatters when I think about Joy. But I'm learning to become friends with that monster pain. It is a grudging, uneasy friendship, like befriending the school bully. But I'm working on it. I'm nurturing my phoenix.

Saturday morning of Thanksgiving weekend, I was having a cup of tea, and yes it was Constant Comment, in the kitchen, staring out the window and thinking about Mrs. Roosevelt's letters. I got to thinking about how human rights begin with human dignity and how that dignity is diminished in so many ways. What Smyth did to me was not right. He should not have gotten away with it. Losing Joy was not right. Babies should be healthy, they should flourish and thrive. All people should be able to flourish and thrive. It shouldn't matter if you are a woman or a baby or if you are Black or whoever. It shouldn't matter who or what you are, your dignity should be respected. I know now that I am going to work for human dignity and women's rights. I am committed to it. I just need to figure out how.

I envy Bruce. He has his plan to go to that ashram in India. You should see him light up when he talks about it. All I see for myself is returning to Roosevelt and trying to find a job. But I can't move home again. There is so much Joy in the house that even though I have moments when I can almost breathe, at other times I remember seeing Joy propped on the sofa or sitting by the table or laying in her playpen and I am crushed with grief. I can't imagine what it must be like for Mama and Aunt Stasia, they were with her every day.

I was sitting, sipping my cup of tea, and thinking about all of that and I guess I was looking forlorn. Mama walked into the kitchen, took one look at me and said she knew how hard it has been for me. She even told me she knew I had been working hard, and she could see that I got a lot from this last semester, especially my course with Dr. Cobbe and seeing Mrs. Roosevelt in the hospital. Yanina, then Mama said, "Joan, I am so very proud of you."

Mama never says stuff like that. But she did. Then she made herself a cup of tea and sat at the kitchen table with me. We were sitting, staring into our tea when Aunt Stasia got home from work at the hospital and burst into the kitchen, "Good, you are both here. I was thinking, Joan, when is graduation?" She took a breath and said, "Joan, I know you are still hurting about Joy. We all are." She took a steadying breath, looked at Mama and me. Then she took a deeper breath and said "But, this is your graduation. You are graduating from Barnard, your dream is coming true. We have to celebrate. We have to have a party. We have to start planning."

Aunt Stasia wants to invite all of Roosevelt, Pamela, Bruce, KarenMarie, all of my friends from my Women in History course, even Dr. Cobbe.

When Aunt Stasia has something on her mind, you know she is a force of nature. The only sane response is to bend with the wind and go with the flow. So, we were off planning my graduation party. Graduation will be at Barnard on Wednesday, January 16, 1963 at 1 o'clock in the afternoon. Mama and Aunt Stasia want to take pictures on campus, and to see some of the city, so we decided to have the party the following weekend, on Sunday the 20th. Aunt Stasia said we should plan to invite people for 5 PM. Mama said she thought Bubba and the ladies from the sewing circle might be willing to help. Aunt Stasia said we would have to be careful or Bubba and the sewing circle might take over the whole shebang. Then Aunt Stasia said, "Some days I am not sure who is prouder of our Joan, us or Mrs. Stein. The rest of the sewing circle comes in a close second in the 'proud of our graduate' line up. We are all so proud of you."

It was embarrassing. I don't know what got into Mama and Aunt Stasia with all those compliments.

And we were back to planning, making an invitation list; writing out a menu; pulling out recipes and making a grocery list; making a timeline detailing what needed to be done, when, and by whom. Aunt Stasia and Mama and their time lines. When they started to break things down to the half hour, I said that I thought they were both getting a little carried away with the planning. They both said, "A good plan" and we all finished "is worth its weight in gold."

That got us all laughing. In our house that is one of those sentences that doesn't even need to be half finished, it has been said so often. I looked at my watch—we spent the entire night planning, and no one bothered about dinner. So, we gathered up our reams of notes, and made ourselves Campbell's tomato soup with milk and chunks of toasted bread floating in it (yes, Aunt Stasia grated parmesan cheese on top of each cup of soup and put it under the broiler the way you like) and naturally, a simple green salad. Even after I went to bed, I could hear Mama and Aunt Stasia in the kitchen drinking tea and making more plans.

Yanina, Dr. Cobbe loves to quote Gloria Steinem. One of her favorite is, "Without dreaming, we lose the excitement of possibilities. Dreaming, after all, is a form of planning." All the day dreams in Mrs. Roosevelt's letters were planning too. I am surrounded by planners.

Yanina, life is so bittersweet. So much has happened this past year. I lost Joy, We all lost Mrs. Roosevelt. The Barnard Bulletin announced that there will be a booth on Jake for 2 weeks were they are accepting contributions for the Barnard donation to the American Association for the United Nations in memory of Mrs. Roosevelt. All of that, and we are planning a party.

After I went to bed, I got melancholy, and started to beat myself up for feeling happy about graduating, and for feeling relieved that I don't have to worry about how I will take care of Joy, and missing her like crazy at the same time. And I remembered the letter Mrs. Roosevelt wrote about her visit to Hiroshima and I thought, if those Japanese people can go on with their lives after an atomic bomb killed so many people and destroyed so much of their country, I guess I can go on with my life too.

People die, everything changes, and life goes on. Camus was right, life is absurd.

And that's the news from Roosevelt, New Jersey. What's your tale, Nightingale? How is life at Kasefet kibbutz? Yanina, I'm sorry that those people from the UNRWA turned down your application. And I know you are frustrated and angry with them, but I know you. You will find a better way to keep working to build a world that is safe for all Jewish people. The work you are doing now is important. You will keep finding new ways to do your work.

Always,

Joan

P.S. So far I have folded close to 500 paper cranes. The apartment in New York is littered with them. Pamela has stitched them together into 6 foot long garlands. So far she has 20 garlands.

Joan to Yanina

January 17, 1963

Dear Yanina,

Papers—finished. Semester—done. And I was dressing for graduation. It was marvelous. I was ready to be cool and indifferent about it. I figured I wouldn't know anybody because I was graduating out of sequence. I thought I would feel like I was out of step. But graduation ceremonies have a power of their own.

We all marched into the auditorium. President Barrows said his welcomes and congratulations. He introduced the Board of Trustees. Then he announced my name as the winter graduation valedictorian. Yanina, I didn't say anything about this before because I didn't believe it would happen. But when I agreed to drop the paternity suit against Smyth, Dr. Cobbe told Barrows we would accede to keeping his 'compromise' quiet if he broke with tradition and there was a valedictorian at this year's winter graduation. We knew my grades guaranteed who the valedictorian would be.

My knees were shaking and my heart was pounding. I could hardly hear what he was saying, I could barely stand. But I walked to the podium and delivered my speech.

Mama and Aunt Stasia both said to keep it short. I did. They also said not to mention Joy. Aunt Stasia said I could mention small 'j' joy. That was hard for me. I wanted to say how special she was, how hard it was to lose her. But they were right. Graduation was a day to celebrate. I thanked Mama, Aunt Stasia, Papa, Dr. Cobbe. I thanked everyone, but not Smyth or Barrows. I talked about endings and beginnings, how even though we learned a lot, there was still a lot we didn't know and we should all keep on learning with our minds and hearts, and as we continue to learn, we should put what we are learning into practice. I talked about living a life of meaning and purpose, trusting happiness to find us if we followed our hearts. I said if we only wanted to be happy we might become self-centered and selfish, but if we only searched for meaning, we might become tedious and miserable.

I wished everyone a life of meaning and happiness. One of my favorite parts was this quote I worked in by Margaret Fuller, from her book *Women in the Nineteenth Century*. Dr. Cobbe says it was the first major feminist book. Margaret Fuller said "If you have knowledge, let others light their candles in it."

I said, now we have knowledge, now we need to let others light their candles in that knowledge, and I wanted to do that by making our world a better place, a place where everyone's dignity is acknowledged and respected. I hoped we would all work to build a world of peace so that nobody's Papa would have to die in war any more. I hoped that there would be peace on earth and I pledged to live a life where peace would begin with me.

I hoped they would all make the same pledge for all of our fathers, brothers, sons and mothers, sisters and daughters, for all of our relatives living and dead and yet to be born. Let there be peace on earth and let it begin with us.

And then there was stone silence.

I thought my speech was a dud. I thought everyone hated it. Bruce and Pamela told me they thought people were not sure if I had finished and were waiting for me to say more. But when I bowed my head, I got a standing ovation, an ovation that echoed through the auditorium. What a moment.

Then it was time for awarding degrees. The Dean called out each of our names. The dean called my name and I practically danced across the stage. When President Barrows handed me my diploma, part of me wanted to kick him for what he tried to do to me, but I let my joy carry me away from him. There was a roar of shouting and applause. I don't know how Mama, Aunt Stasia, Pamela and Bruce did it, but the whole auditorium echoed—for me. Over it all I could hear Bruce shouting out, "Joan of Roosevelt." Finally, finally, finally I am a Barnard graduate.

There are things I will miss: hearing new ideas, talking in Jake and scanning the posters, hanging in the quad on a sunny day, listening to Dr. Cobbe and some of my other professors. There are things I will miss. But the taste of freedom is ice cream on a hot summer day. I am a free woman for the first time in my life. My heart is dancing.

Mama, Aunt Stasia and I are staying in New York to clean out my stuff from the apartment and to be tourists in New York to celebrate. We did not have to do a lot of clearing because Pamela is keeping the apartment while she finishes her graduate work. We will drive home on Sunday for my party. The entire town is coming. The Klezevelts, Roosevelt's very own Klezmer Band, will be there. Yanina, I wish you could be here.

But I will write and tell you all about it.

Always,

Joan

Joan to Yanina

January 22, 1963

Dear Yanina,

After our vacation days in New York, we drove into Roosevelt on route 571 and a huge hand painted banner was hanging across Homestead Lane

Joan of Roosevelt
*Mazel Tov*
Congratulations to Our Graduate.

Bruce has everyone calling me Joan of Roosevelt.

I read that sign and it was like I got a hug from everyone in Roosevelt. For a minute it was like the troubles of last year didn't happen.

But then we pulled up to our house, and it all came back to me in a tidal wave. Smyth becoming Harold to me, my being pregnant, my filing the paternity suit against Smyth, Barrows blackmailing me to drop my paternity suit against Smyth. Giving birth to my beautiful Joy, losing my Joy, my sweet, beautiful baby. Yanina, we pulled up to the house, and I sat there in the back seat of the car and cried. I was sobbing and couldn't stop. I sat there and cried.

Aunt Stasia parked the car, and she and Mama got out, came and sat on either side of me. They held me and let me cry. For once they didn't ask, they sat there quietly with me. I cried enough to flood Assunpink Lake, wiped my eyes, blew my nose, took a deep breath and said, "OK." We carried my stuff into the house as if nothing happened.

We walked into the house and my heart dropped. There were no decorations, nothing set up. Did that mean nobody was coming? But why did they even bother with the sign on route 571? I guess Aunt Stasia could read my face because she scrunched up her face into that frown that is more like a smile and told me that so many people were coming to the party, they had to move it to the school. My party would be under the mural. Bubba made a sign with directions to hang on our front door so my friends could find their way down the street. It wasn't that nobody was coming. It was that everybody was coming and bringing friends to celebrate my commencement, the beginning of the rest of my life.

The rest of my life—that is a thought. What will I do with the rest of my life? Mrs. Roosevelt wrote about Clare Boothe Luce's toast at her 70th birthday party, "Comfort the distressed, and distress the comfortable." (I'm sending you that letter.) I would love to do that.

Mama, Aunt Stasia and I walked down the street to the school. The whole town was waiting. We walked in the door and there was an overwhelming roar of applause and cheering. Right there in front was Bubba. Yanina, she was her old self again. She was beaming in her Bubba way. Sara from the post office was there, Mama's sewing circle ladies, even Fannie, everyone. Off to the side I saw Pamela, Bruce, KarenMarie, Rebecca, Kevin, Patricia, Rita, Gregory, Sylvia, Sandy and Curtis, the whole crew from Women in History. Dr. Cobbe was beaming. Rabbi Katzeck was there. As soon as the cheering stopped, the Klezevelts played, "*Sto Lat*." Mama started to cry, she said she was proud of me. I was glowing like a 150 watt light bulb. Everyone was there, everyone was jubilant.

Everybody was hugging Mama, Aunt Stasia and me. Everybody was hugging everybody. It was a crazy, chaotic tangle of people. I hugged my way through the tangle to the gang from school and to Dr. Cobbe (who for once didn't smell of cats). She gave me her gratified advisor smile, took my hands and said that I should be proud of myself, that she was proud of me. She said graduating summa cum laude, highest honors, and valedictorian of the graduating class was never easy and she knew it had been particularly challenging for me with the year I had, so I should be especially proud of myself. She said that she will miss our conversations, that she will miss me, and that she hopes I will stay in touch—and we should talk soon because she wants me to apply for a fellowship with her for the fall semester.

I promised I would. Then I was caught up in the school crowd, Patricia and KarenMarie were congratulating me, and Kevin and Gregory were saying something, I noticed Curtis staring at the wall. I elbowed Patricia, who nudged KarenMarie, who poked Kevin, Bruce and around the group we went until we were all looking at Curtis standing there with the biggest eyes I have ever seen, staring at our mural. We were all enjoying the look of awe and amazement on Curtis' face when I notice Ben Shahn a few people away from us. I slipped over to him and asked him if I could introduce a friend of mine to him. The mural and Ben are part of life in Roosevelt. I forget to be impressed. Ben noticed Curtis' expression and said, "I've got this."

Ben slipped over to our group and stood next to Curtis. Ben asked Curtis if he liked the mural. Curtis didn't blink, didn't stop staring at the mural, he said, "It's a fresco not a mural. That fresco is totally unreal, eighteen karat, righteous." Ben laughed, "Thank you, young man. It is indeed a fresco. Around here we are informal about it and refer to it as the mural. I'm delighted that you are enjoying my work."
You should have seen the look on Curtis' face. He almost fell over. He stuttered, "Mr. Shahn. Oh, Mr. Shahn. You are amazing. So amazing. You are an honor. I am an honor. I mean I am honored to meet you . . ." He went on and on. He tried to kiss Ben's hand. Ben kept laughing. Then the two of them were talking art, poetry and literature. Curtis was telling Ben about the novel he is writing when I escaped.

Pamela asked if I was going to wear my coat all night. I hadn't even realized I was still wearing it. She took my coat. We collected Mama and Aunt Stasia's coats and took them to the coat room. We finished hanging up all the coats, and Pamela gave me a great big congratulations hug. I was hugging her back, thanking her for being there with me through everything, when Bubba walked in with an arm full of coats. Yanina, it was weird, Bubba looked at the two of us hugging each other and said, "Oy! The apple doesn't fall far from the tree!" And she was laughing her head off. I've never seen Bubba laugh like that. There were tears in her eyes she was laughing so hard.

My mouth was hanging open. "What?" I asked her?

And she laughed even harder. "I know."

"What?"

"I know."

"You know what?"

"Oh, Joan, I know. Who do you think told your Mother and your Aunt Stasia about Ruth and Naomi? Who do you think showed them the Book of Ruth, 'Where ever you go, I will go.' You know those lines? I was the one who taught them to your Mother. Your Mother and Aunt Stasia are Roosevelt's Ruth and Naomi."

Then Pamela was laughing and saying, "I knew it. I knew it when I first met them."

I asked Pamela, "What are you both talking about?"

Bubba rolled her eyes and said, "Sure, OK. But come now girls, Rebbi is waiting with the blessing. People are looking for you, Joan. Come and celebrate."

Yanina, what don't I know? Why am I always the last one to know everything?

Bubba didn't give me a minute to think. She swept us into the throng of the crowd. Rabbi Katzeck called Mama, Aunt Stasia and me to the table. He clanged the school bell. They still use that old thing to change classes. People quieted down. Rabbi Katzeck cleared his throat and made a speech about my accomplishments, and how proud the town is of me, then he said, "Mazel tov. Congratulations to you and your family, your Mother Eva and your Aunt Anastasia. Mazel tov Joan." More cheers and clapping. It was embarrassing and wonderful.

Rabbi Katzeck talked about commencement as the beginning of the next stage of my life, he gave thanks, and the party began in earnest. There was music, dancing and eating until the sun came up. Nobody in Roosevelt did any work that Monday. Mama, Aunt Stasia and I slept in until noon. Pamela slept on the couch in the living room. Bruce slept on the floor in Bubba's living room.

Rabbi Katzeck was right. When I woke up, it was not only a new day, it was a whole new chapter in my life. How will I comfort the distressed, and distress the comfortable? How will I work for women's human rights? Those are real questions now. Not that I haven't thought about them before. But now, now I need to figure out how to live out my answers to those questions.

I was sitting at the kitchen table thinking and Aunt Stasia came in to perk coffee. She took one look at me and said her Buddhist thing, "Joan, life and death are grave matters. All things in life pass away quickly. Each of us must be alert, never neglectful and never indulgent." Then she said graduation from college is a once in a lifetime accomplishment, and I should give myself time to enjoy the moment, today let my heart be light and enjoy my friends.

Pamela and Bruce came into the kitchen, Pamela asked us if we wanted to go in to Barnard for Dr. Cobbe's workshop. She reminded us that Dr. Cobbe invited representatives from President Kennedy's Peace Corps to come and do a presentation. Pamela said that she might be interested in joining the Peace Corps after she finishes grad school.
I had forgotten about the workshop. Mama and Aunt Stasia both looked at me and said, "The Peace Corps?" I told them I was only going to keep Bruce and Pamela from signing up. And I owed it to Dr. Cobbe to show up. We got there just in time. The Peace Corps does amazing work, but it is not for me.

After the presentation, Dr. Cobbe pulled me aside and said that she has funding for a fellowship in the fall for a graduate student to work with her on developing a women's studies program at Barnard. She wants me to apply. She thinks it would be fun for the two of us to work together. I would have to apply for a graduate program too. She said Columbia has a master of social work degree that I could apply to and still work with her on her fellowship. That is something to think about.

I know I want to work for women's human rights, social work could be a way to do that.

Always,

Joan

From ER to Eva

October 15, 1954

Dear Eva,

Monday was my 70th birthday. I am not one for big celebrations, but I let myself be persuaded to assent to a fund-raiser for the American Association for the United Nations (AAUN) on this occasion. The event had far too much falderal for me, but it was successful in raising much needed money for the AAUN and for that I was willing to put up with some fluff and circumstance.

One highlight of the evening that I enjoyed immensely was the toast offered by Miss Clare Boothe Luce, the playwright and Ambassador to Italy. She said, "Here's to Eleanor. No woman has ever so comforted the distressed, or so distressed the comfortable." I laughed so hard I thought I might spill my sparking water. Indeed, she summed up my best dream for my ambitions in that one sentence.

Eva, I may be seventy, but in my heart I am young and vibrant and full of hope for our country and for our world. I believe that I still have a few more years of comforting the distressed and distressing the comfortable in me. I still harbor the hope that in this new era of human rights, peace may yet become a reality.

Oh Eva, young Joan and Yanina are blossoming into headstrong young women. Joan is already a freshman in high school? And she is still nurturing her dream of attending Barnard College? You seem to have resigned yourself to that. And Yanina is still talking about moving to Israel after high school? At least Joan is not planning to join her friend in that venture!

With hope for our future and always with love, your affectionate friend,

Eleanor

# *Part VI*
# *Life after College*

Joan to Yanina

February 19, 1963

Dear Yanina,

I am overjoyed that you are pregnant. You and Simcha must be in seventh heaven. Mazel Tov to you both.

When are you due? How are you doing? Tell me everything. Willa Cather had it right, "Happiness is to be dissolved into something true and complete and great." You having a baby, that is as true and complete and great as anything can ever be. I am so happy for you. I wish we were not oceans apart, so we could all celebrate together. There are so many things I wish could be different. But, happiness is so ephemeral, so evanescent, we should celebrate yours without the tarnish of my wishes. So, Mazel Tov to you my heart-sister, my friend.

Back here at Roosevelt, well, a week after the party, I was sitting in the kitchen drinking a cup of tea (sometimes it feels like all I do is drink tea when I am at home in Roosevelt). I was thinking about the party and Mama walked into the kitchen. She sat down and I heard myself telling her about when Pamela and I were hanging our coats up in the coat closet at the party—how Pamela was hugging me saying congratulations on my speech and graduation; how Bubba walked in and looked at us, said the apple doesn't fall far from the tree, and that Mama and Aunt Stasia were like Ruth and Naomi.

I told Mama that I asked Bubba what she meant, but Bubba rushed us out of the closet because Rabbi Katzek was waiting to give the blessing. Then the night got crazy, and I never got a chance to ask Bubba what she meant.

I asked Mama if she knew what Bubba was talking about. I said I read about Ruth and Naomi, and they were a daughter- and mother-in-law. I asked Mama what that had to do with her and Aunt Stasia. When I finished talking Mama looked nervous and flustered. What did I expect? I mean, Mama was never one for deep intimate conversations.

Mama actually looked a little frightened. But I had asked the questions, and I could see she was searching for a way to an answer. She sat up a little straighter, smiled, frowned, then half smiled and said, "We better make ourselves a pot of tea."

As we sat with our tea Mama said, "Joan, there is something you don't know. It's not that we, that I, ever meant to keep it a secret from you. I thought we should wait until you were old enough. Then I wanted to find the right moment, but the right moment never seemed to be there. But, I love you Joan, you know that don't you?"

As she said all that I started to get frightened, but I nodded yes.

Mama took a deep breath and said, "Joan, there is no one that your Aunt Stasia or I love more than you. We have both dedicated our lives to keeping you safe and swaddled in our love so you can be strong in your spirit and body, so you can find your place in the world, one that is true to your heart and your soul. Those may be Stasia's words, Joan, but they have their root in my heart. We both want you to be strong and safe and happy. You know that, don't you?"

I don't know why, but my eyes filled up with tears, I said, "Yes."

"Joan. . . You know how you say that Aunt Stasia and I are closer than best friends? You see that's just it. We are closer than best friends. We have become much more than best friends. Ruth and Naomi were mother-in-law and daughter-in-law. But they were also two women who loved each other. Joan, like Ruth and Naomi, your Aunt Stasia and I love each other. If we could marry each other, we would. But we can't."
I sat there thinking a man and a woman get married, but Mama and Aunt Stasia are both women. I kept thinking that for a while, then, I got it. Finally I woke up and got it.

Yanina, how oblivious can I be. Mama looked at her hands in her lap and said, "Joan, your Aunt and I have always been close friends. We always loved to spend time together. We were best friends, more than best friends. We joked about being soul mates. Joan, Anastasia and I are in love with each other.

"After Brony, your Papa, was killed in the war, Stasia was spending more and more time here, helping me with things. We relied on each other more and more. We were both heartbroken those months after Brony died. We would fall asleep crying in each other's arms. One thing led to another, and . . ."

Yanina, at that point I said I didn't need any more details. I started to laugh, it was nervous laughter at first, but it grew into belly laughter, big bubbling belly laughter—mostly at myself. Sometimes I amaze myself with how oblivious I can be. Relationships befuddle me. I can understand a lot of things. I'm good with books at school, but when it comes to what goes on between people, I'm just obtuse.

Through my laughing, I said, "I was raised by two lesbians and never noticed. I could have been raised by wolves and I wouldn't have noticed."

Yanina I said it, and then I remembered the picnic where Aunt Stasia reminded Mama how Papa used to laugh about being raised by wolves and I wanted to take my words back. But before I could say anything, Mama's eyes softened, and she laughed. She said, "Joan, your Papa used to say that he sometimes thought he could have been raised by wolves. Sometimes you remind me of him more than I can bear. And I am always glad that you do. You Papa was a free spirit, and I loved that about him. I'm happy to see you starting to embrace your free spirit Joan, it does my heart good." Mama hugged me, and we were both laughing so hard we were crying.

Yanina, how long have I been trying to stifle any trace of my free spirit to keep Mama from thinking about Papa and crying, only to find out now that seeing it in me makes her happy! Now I'm thinking it is time to relax and just be who I am, whoever that is.

And! What do they call it? Coming Out of the Closet? I asked Mama about Bubba's comments in the closet, and Mama came Out of the Closet to me! How did I not notice anything? Pitiful? Ironic? Funny? But I am kind of exasperated that they never told me.

There was a second condolence letter to Mama from Mrs. Roosevelt in the bag. I'm sending it to you. It never made much sense to me. I wondered why Mrs. Roosevelt was talking about being in love. I wondered if Mama might have been in love with someone. I wondered what happened to that person. But now when I reread it, I wonder how I didn't see the truth.

I was raised by two lesbians and I never noticed. I am so much better at seeing what's going on in books. I am so much better at understanding books than people.

Yanina, I don't know what I will do next, but I've got options. I will take the time I need to think them through. I could apply to the Peace Corps and help people in another country. I could go to India with Bruce. Yesterday I saw an ad in the Barnard Bulletin for a service learning trip to Israel—I would be near you. That fellowship with Dr. Cobbe is interesting. But I've been in school for 16 years straight, I might need a break from books and studying.

But I understand books. I'm good with books. For now I'm going back to the apartment in New York to live with Pamela. I know I don't want to live in Roosevelt.

What's your tale, Nightingale? I'm so happy that you are pregnant.

Always,

Joan

From ER to Eva

May 10, 1945

Dear Eva,

Two days ago our world declared victory in Europe, and the country is celebrating. But so much of our old way of life has been permanently altered. Your dear Bronislaw and my Franklin have both lost their lives in the past year. With aching hearts we move on to build new lives. Even as you grieve your Bronislaw, you and Anastasia have found solace with each other amidst your grieving. The ways that sorrow and happiness braid themselves together is one of the great enigmas of life.

My Dear Eva, when it comes to love, you must keep your heart open. You must follow as your hearts lead you, even though you are unsure how you feel regarding such things. The heart has a clarity of its own. Love in all of its myriad forms is to be cherished and nurtured. When you find someone you love, the only right and true thing is to love that person fully and completely with all the courage, strength, joy and openness you can find. Love and friendship are to be cherished.

Eva, I have found it desirable to be circumspect and discrete regarding my most intimate relationships. What is between friends best remains between friends. Yes, welcome and cherish love when and where you find it, but be practical and realistic in recognizing that our social world does not hold every manifestation of love in its best regard. I find it wise to be open with my love and circumspect in my social circle.

You will continue to grieve the passing of your Bronislaw. Our grieving for a dear loved one never leaves us, but it does change in intensity and in character. Even as you remember your Bronislaw, you must live your life, and live it fully.

Thank you for asking after the children. They are as fractious as ever. I worry for my boys overseas. I worry for all our boys overseas and I pray they will be home soon.

My hope for you is that you will emerge from these days of grieving and crisis with a deepened sense of purpose and vitality. I am heartened that you have found in your Anastasia a source of consolation and tenderness.

With love, your affectionate friend

Eleanor

Joan to Yanina

March 25, 1963

Dear Yanina,

I am back in New York living with Pamela in our old apartment. It's like I never left, except everything is different. Mama and Aunt Stasia and I are closer than ever now.
Every time I think about Mama and Aunt Stasia being a couple, I chuckle. KarenMarie and I were having coffee the other day, and I told her it still miffed me that Mama and Aunt Stasia never told me. She rolled her eyes and said, "When is the best time to tell your daughter she is being raised by two lesbians? Not when she is a kid —you don't want her telling other kids at school. Not when she is an adolescent—that is hard enough for a girl, with all those raging hormones. On Washington's Day because he never told a lie?—too corny." I was laughing then and KarenMarie said, "It's not like there is a National Coming Out Day." Maybe there should be.

And, you are so right, only I could read that letter from Mrs. Roosevelt where she tells Mama to be discreet about who she loves and not see what she was talking about!

Pamela, Bruce and I have been talking about our futures. Pamela is determined to get her Ph.D. so she can become a college professor. And, you will love this, Bruce's sister, Rhoda, got accepted into Columbia's graduate program in history. She and Pamela are in some of the same classes. They study together—a lot. Even I can see that they like each other—a lot. Watching them trying to be discreet is fun. Bruce is still going to India, but he is not as enthusiastic about it. He and I are spending more time alone together while Pamela and Rhoda are studying.

I don't think I appreciated how sweet and special he is when it was the three of us hanging out.

Always,

Joan

Joan to Yanina

April 17, 1963

You know I needed to get a job now that I am out of school. It didn't take me long to discover there is not an enormous demand for history majors. Kelly Girls always have an ad in the Barnard Bulletin, but I couldn't picture myself working in an office typing and filing all day. Then I saw an ad in the Amsterdam News for nursing assistants at St. Luke's Hospital, across the street from Barnard. I can walk there from the apartment. The ad said I would be helping sick people get healthy. There was an opening on the grave yard shift. I thought it would be quiet in the hospital that late at night, most of the patients would be sleeping. I thought I might even have a little time to read. It seemed perfect. I applied, and they hired me on April 1.

You won't believe what happened two nights ago. At 2:10 AM the call bell went off for room 308. The charge nurse looked up from writing her chart notes and said, "You're up Joan."

The lady in room 308 was a big, big lady, just back from surgery. She was still groggy from the anesthesia, and she had to go. I got the bed pan, rolled her on her side, and eased her down the way they showed us. Man-oh-Manischewitz, she filled that bedpan to the brim. I got it out from under her, covered it with the blue pad, and oh so carefully carried it down the hall to the flusher room. All without spilling a drop.

One of the housekeeping ladies was in there cleaning. She said something to me, but I couldn't hear her over the radio that was blaring out an old speech by Mrs. Roosevelt.
I put the bedpan in the flusher.

Mrs. Roosevelt was saying, "Universal human rights begin in small places, close to home. . . the places where every man, woman and child seeks equal justice, equal opportunity, equal dignity."

I closed the bedpan flusher and pulled the handle.
The next thing I knew the flusher blew open, and I was covered in shit from head to toe.

There was no sign saying the flusher was broken.

Without opening my mouth I said, "Oh shit."

The housekeeping lady said, "No shit. I told you the latch was broken."

I never heard her. All I heard was, "All people have a right to dignity."

We laughed. I didn't dare open my mouth, but I couldn't help laughing.

We were both laughing so hard we were crying. The lady got me a towel and said, "Honey, life is full of shit. Now and then, it hits you full in the face. But you gotta get up, take a shower and move on. Go take yourself a good long shower. I'll tell the charge nurse."

Three showers later, the smell of shit and Mrs. Roosevelt assertion of the right to dignity still echoed in my head. I love the letter I'm sending you where she quotes from that speech.

My life is so absurd. Saint Paul's epiphany came with lightning. My epiphany came with a shower of shit. Classic.
But nothing can stop me now. I am going to apply for that fellowship with Dr. Cobbe and to the social work program at Columbia. I will be working with Dr. Cobbe on women's studies and getting a master's degree in helping people. I've found a way to work for women's rights and dignity. I talked with Dr. Cobbe yesterday and she said I have an excellent chance at the fellowship and at getting into Columbia. She will write a recommendation for me and that will carry a lot of weight since the fellowship is with her. I talked with Mama and she thinks the Roosevelt Scholarship will cover my graduate degree. I'm on my way.

What's your tale, Nightingale? How are you doing? I am so excited for you and Simcha.

Always,

Joan

From ER to Eva

December 12, 1958

Dear Eva,

Your Joan is finishing her freshman year at Barnard, she is just beginning her life, and I am more and more feeling my age. I am increasingly aware that my time on this earth is short. And that is perfectly fine with me. I have lived long and well. I have accomplished many of my goals. My work at the United Nations is one of the things that brings me the greatest satisfaction and hope. I still delight in the moment when the *Universal Declaration of Human Rights* was ratified by the General Assembly.

Two days ago we celebrated the tenth anniversary of the passage of that Declaration. I want to share with you part of a speech I made as we celebrated its passage.

*Where, after all, do human rights begin? In small places, close to home, so close and so small that they cannot be seen on any maps of the world. Yet they are the world of the individual person; the neighborhood he lives in; the school or college he attends; the factory, farm or office where he works. Such are the places where every man, woman and child seeks equal justice, equal opportunity, equal dignity without discrimination. Unless these rights have meaning there, they have little meaning anywhere. Without concerned citizen action to uphold them close to home, we shall look in vain for progress in the larger world.*

Eva, as I write this letter to you, I find myself reflecting on our years of writing to each other. I was in my middle fifties, you were in your early 20s when we first began our correspondence. As my final chapter draws to a close and you approach your middle years, I wonder about the life you will have. I hope your life is filled with the best of your dreams. I hope you keep your heart and spirit open to joy and laughter. I hope your life is rich and rewarding, that your love is deep, and that you will always be open to the possibilities that present themselves to you as you move in the small places close to home, even as you discover the grandeur of our world.

With love, your affectionate friend,

Eleanor

Joan to Yanina

May 9, 1963

Dear Yanina,

You and Simcha are coming home to Roosevelt! I can't wait to see you. Bubba is Bubbaling over. She has cleaned the house six times over. She wants to start cooking for you and Simcha. Mama and Aunt Stasia can barely slow her down. They have her writing out menus and grocery lists instead. Yanina, she has two months of menus worked out for when you and Simcha get home. I hope you have an appetite.

And, there is more to celebrate.

The day before yesterday my letter came from Columbia University. They accepted me into their Masters of Social Work program for the fall, and I got the fellowship with Dr. Cobbe. The fellowship and the Roosevelt Scholarship will cover all of my graduate school expenses!

And there is even more amazing news.

I showed Bruce my letter from Columbia, and he took me to this amazing Indian restaurant, the Maharaja Palace, to celebrate.

After we ordered dessert, Bruce walked around the table so he was standing next to me, then he got down on one knee, took my hands in his and he said, "Joan, when I return from India, all my exploring will be to arrive where I started, with you my Joan of Roosevelt. I want to build my home, my life together with you as husband and wife. Joan of Roosevelt, with all my being, with all my consciousness, I love you. You are my best friend, my soulmate, my bliss."

He even quoted Eleanor Roosevelt, "There are people who walk in and out of our lives, but only true friends leave footprints on our hearts." Then he said, "Joan, the path of your footprints are my heart's treasure. Will you walk the path of life with me? Will you be my wife?"

Yanina, I was speechless—for a second, long enough to realize that Bruce is not only a dear friend, but that I couldn't imagine him not being at the center of my life. I have been falling in love with him since we met in Dr. Cobbe's class.
Of course I said yes.

Oh, Yanina, I am so totally, completely over the moon. Mama, Aunt Stasia and Bubba are beside themselves. They danced! I told them I was a shocked that Bruce proposed, that I thought of him as my best friend, but not my boyfriend. They said they were shocked it took him so long to get around to it. I really am the last one to see what's going on in a relationship.

Bruce will go to the Ashram for a year. I will use the year to focus in on my graduate work. Dr. Cobbe said Columbia's social work degree is a two-year program. (Yanina, Frances Perkins, President Roosevelt's Secretary of Labor was a graduate of Columbia's social work program. The Roosevelts are everywhere in my life.) I will be half way through the program when Bruce returns from India. We will figure out the details of where and when we are getting married when he gets home (if Mama, Aunt Stasia and Bubba haven't worked it all out by then).

And, Yanina, you are coming home. I can't wait to see you. All is right with the world. Pamela says my life is FINE: festive, ineffable, notable, ebullient. I don't know if I would go that far, but I am happier than I have been in a long time. Last year being this happy would frighten me. Now I am basking in the moment. If this past year has taught me anything, it has taught me to cherish happiness where and when you find it.

Have a safe flight. Aunt Stasia and I will meet you and Simcha at the airport.

Always,

Joan

# *Epilogue*

Joan Zatańczy Sharma in Roosevelt, NJ to her daughter Anna Sharma at Oberlin College, Oberlin, Ohio

October 8, 1986

Dear Anna,

It seems like your father and I just brought you home from the hospital, and on Saturday, Eleanor Roosevelt's 100th birthday, you will turn twenty-one. Your father says, the way Eleanor Roosevelt echoes throughout my life, you couldn't have been born on any other day. We were married on December 10, 1964, sixteen years to the day after Mrs. Roosevelt's *Universal Declaration of Human Rights* was ratified; of course our daughter was born on her birthday.

When you were born, your father whispered one of her quotes in my ear, "At a child's birth, if a mother could ask a fairy godmother to endow the child with the most useful gift, that gift would be curiosity." Together we wished that for you., and you are the most curious girl ever. It goes to show—be careful what you wish for.

And now you are turning twenty-one. But you will always be our baby girl.

On my twenty-first birthday, my mother gave me a bag of letters from Eleanor Roosevelt, a trove of her experiences, observations and ideas. As I read those letters, I became obsessed with human rights and dignity.

Those letters transformed my life during my last two years at Barnard. Mrs. Roosevelt and those letters taught me the importance of developing my potentials to their utmost and contributing my best to our world with unfettered enthusiasm.

Now I am sending that bag of letters to you for your twenty-first birthday. I wonder how they will touch you. As I was wrapping the bag for you, I found myself thinking about the years since I turned twenty-one.

Your father and I have had some grand adventures since we met in Dr. Cobbe's Women in History course at Barnard. India was good for your father, meeting Mother Teresa, the Ashram learning *yogas*, learning that yoga means discipline. I know you can hear us in your sleep: me wondering about the meaning of life; your father quoting Mother Teresa, "Be helpful. Do small things with great love." That is the meaning of life in full measure for him. When he came home from India and started to teach a few yoga classes, no one thought the classes would last. The classes flourished. He opened a yoga studio, and no one thought that would last. Now his three yoga studios are flourishing.

Reading the letters from Mrs. Roosevelt, motivate my work for women's dignity and human rights. When I was doing my fellowship with Dr. Cobbe, she arranged an internship for me with the United Nations Commission on the Status of Women, analyzing data to assess the status of women in countries around the world. Twenty-two years later I am still working with the Commission. After you and your father, my work with the Commission is my great love.

Your Aunt Yanina still laughs at the irony of my getting a job with the United Nations. There was a time she wanted to work with the United Nations Relief and Works Agency for Palestinian refugees. They turned her down because she was living in an Israeli kibbutz near the Gaza strip. But teaching is a good career for your Aunt Yanina. Through her teaching about the Holocaust, she is building a world safe for all Jews.

Anna, I wish you had gotten to meet Zayde. He was a *mensch* if there ever was one. No one had more integrity than our Zayde. I am glad that Bubba got to know you and your cousins Moshe, Shoshana and Janosik before her stroke. I don't think she was ever happier than when she was pushing a baby carriage along Homestead Lane.

Grandma Eva and Granny Stasia, both send their love. Granny Stasia finally got Grandma Eva to go with her into New York City to volunteer with the Gay Men's Health Crisis. Granny Stasia is afraid that gay cancer thing will become something bad. You should hear Granny Stasia and KarenMarie when they get together. KarenMarie is outraged at the way crack cocaine is ravaging Harlem, Granny Stasia is outraged at how gay cancer is ravaging Greenwich Village.

They are both outraged and working to change things.

Anna, you have your whole life in front of you. As I think about you turning twenty-one, I wonder where your life will take you, what you will make of your life, who you will find to love and build your life with. My birthday wish for you is that you will continue becoming a woman of strong purpose in the spirit of your eponym.

When I was your age I was obsessed with finding the meaning of life, the meaning of my life. I took a philosophy course, thinking that might help me in my search. I learned that Aristotle believed thinking about the good life was premature for the young whose emotions are out of control and who lack the experience to understand what it means to flourish; and Camus said life is absurd because we live in an infinite and uncaring cosmos. I was so frustrated with that course. It was the only A- I ever got at Barnard.

Now I see that the meaning of life is not something you search for and find, it is something you build. All the commitment, dedication, energy and grit that you pour into working for the larger purpose you have dedicated our life to—that is the meaning of life. Aristotle was right, you can only recognize that when you are able to look back and see the landscape and the path you have carved across your days. Camus was right when he said the cosmos is vast, but each life does have its place, its role; each life is significant in its own way. As Mrs. Roosevelt used to say, "We do not have to become heroes (or find the meaning of our lives) overnight. Just one step at a time."

Once I asked your Granny Stasia about the meaning of life, she told me she came to peace with her search for meaning when she realized that her life is nothing more than one drop in a cosmic sneeze. One evening while she was meditating, she sneezed and saw a drop from her sneeze floating in the wind; she saw the beauty of the moon reflected in it and realized that was enough, that was everything. That is your Granny Stasia for you. Be careful what you ask your Granny, because you will most certainly get a crumpled bit of wisdom as an answer.

Thinking about your birthday has got me thinking about how quickly time passes. Your father and I have been married for twenty-two years. Aunties Pamela and Rhoda have been together for twenty-three years. KarenMarie has been working with Angela Davis for twenty-four years. Aunt Yanina and Uncle Simcha celebrated their twenty-fifth anniversary last year. Grandma Eva and Granny Stasia are both sixty-five, but they both insist they are too young to retire. They have been together nearly forty years.

I wonder who you will find to love, what challenges the years will bring to you.

So many things have changed. But, as your Granny Stasia is fond of saying, “Impermanence is the fragrance of our days.” (I thought that was one of her Buddhist sayings, but yesterday I read it in Rainer Maria Rilke’s Sonnets to Orpheus.) Impermanence may be the fragrance of our days, but as Grandma Eva says, “Salad is the essence and the sustenance of our beings.”

Anna, as I look back at our lives—your Grannies, Aunt Yanina & Uncle Simcha, Aunties Pamela and Rhoda, KarenMarie, your father and I—our lives are not perfect, but they are complete and we are fulfilled. We have all found our purpose and meaning, each in our way: Grandma Eva in logic and reason, Granny Stasia through harmony with nature, Zayde and Bubba through their faith, Aunt Pamela and KarenMarie though their activism and autonomy, your Papa and I in our family and community. All of us, in our way, are finding our way to loving more fully, as we grow in wisdom and compassion. Auntie Pamela says all of us are FINE: Feisty, impassioned, normal-ish, enduring.

As you stand on the precipice of adulthood, I hope that when you reach middle age where I stand now, you will be able to say that about your life as well.

Now, I'd better get going and help with supper, I hear your father out in the kitchen cutting the vegetables and singing his version of T. S. Eliot's "Happy Gidding." It will always be his favorite lullaby for you. He still says Elliot's vision of finding salvation in the unity of the past, present and future is one more iteration of his father's story about Indra's web and the interdependence of all things. Your father!

He says to tell you he is singing you his favorite verses:

All of our exploring
Will be to arrive where we started,
At home in Roosevelt,
To know that place for the first time.
And all shall be well,
All manner of things shall be well.

Happy 21st birthday, our dear daughter.

Always,

Your Mama & Papa

*Letters from Eleanor Roosevelt* is Mary's debut novel. However, she has published nonfiction books and articles in the areas of social justice, human rights, feminism, and LGBTQ issues. Mary also gathers stories, allegories, and fables about strong women, social justice and human rights at JustAlchemy.com. She enjoys reading historical novels, mysteries, fantasy and retold fairy tales. When she is not writing or curled up with a good book, you can find her kayaking the flat waters of Cape Cod or enjoying a conversation, food, and maybe a glass of wine with friends.

Mary is an Emeritus faculty member at the School of Social Work at Monmouth University. She has earned a BA in politics from de Sales University, Center Valley, Pa; an M.S.W. from Marywood University, Scranton, Pa; a Ph.D. in social work from Rutgers, the State University, New Brunswick, New Jersey.

You can find out more about Mary's writing at MarySwigonski.com where you can subscribe to her newsletter, or on twitter @MarySwig.

# Distinguishing Fact from Fiction

In an earlier iteration of my life, I taught college level social work. One day Dr. Janice Wood Wetzel, from Adelphi University and I were having lunch, and I asked her opinion about the role of social justice in social work. Janice said social justice is important, but she thought human rights are more central to social work practice, because they are more specific and concrete. She said, "I could wax poetic about human rights." I urged her to do so. She did, and that conversation changed my life.

I read everything I could about human rights. That reading introduced me to the work of Eleanor Roosevelt. At one point I read an apocryphal story alleging that after Franklin died and Harry Truman took office, Truman wasn't sure what to do with Eleanor. She wielded too much informal power in Washington and was too popular among everyday people throughout the country. Because she was so popular, he needed to give her a public role, but he wanted her out of his way. So he sent her to Europe to work with the United Nations; that got her out of the country and out of his hair. Except, Eleanor's power and popularity grew internationally with her work at the United Nations. That story solidified Mrs. Roosevelt's place as a hero for me.

When I read Mary Ann Glendon's *A World Made New: Eleanor Roosevelt and the Universal Declaration of Human Rights*, I was taken with Mrs. Roosevelt's role as negotiator-in-chief of drafting of the Declaration.

The more I read about Mrs. Roosevelt, the more I discovered the extent of her letter writing. She wrote thousands of letters. If you wrote to her, she answered your letter. It didn't matter who you were, she answered your letter. Mrs. Bertha Brodsky from Brooklyn, NY wrote to her telling Mrs. Roosevelt about her need for back surgery so she could get a job, surgery that she could not afford. Mrs. Roosevelt not only wrote to Mrs. Brodsky, she arranged the surgery, attended her wedding and became godmother to her child.

I read about President Roosevelt's subsistence homestead program, and Mrs. Roosevelt's engagement with the Arthurdale Homestead Project in West Virginia. As I explored the locations of other Homestead Projects, I discovered Jersey Homesteads which is about an hour from where I live in New Jersey. I also learned that a small group of women from Jersey Homesteads wrote to Mrs. Roosevelt about difficulties that the town was having with their factory. I found a record of the letter having been written. But I could find no record of a response.

All of those elements fed my imagination. This book is the result.

Because the book is salted with historical characters and references to events in their lives, I thought I should highlight some of the boundary lines between fact and fiction. Jersey Homestead/ Roosevelt, New Jersey and Barnard College are actual places, but they are used fictionally. Kasefet Kibbutz was inspired by Kissufim Kibbutz in Israel.

All the letters in the book are fictional. Eva, Bronislaw, Joan and Anastasia Zatańczy, Yanina and Simcha Kominiarski are all fictional characters, as are the residents of Jersey Homestead/ Roosevelt, New Jersey, and Kasefet kibbutz.
Barnard College never had a President Barrows and all the characters, actions and events described there are fictional. Withey Hall does not exist on Barnard's campus.

Clearly Mrs. Eleanor Roosevelt is an actual historical person. From 1926 to 1933, while Franklin was governor of New York, she owned the Todhunter School in NYC with Marion Dickerman and Nancy Cook and taught history and government there. That may well have been one of her favorite jobs.

Mrs. Roosevelt traveled to the Gila River Internment Camp, but the descriptions of her actions and experiences there are all fictional. Mrs. Roosevelt was one of the United States representatives to the United Nations and she chaired the committee that drafted the United Nations *Universal Declaration of Human Rights*. She delivered a speech at the Sorbonne in Paris. But all descriptions of actions and thoughts related to those events are fiction.

Mrs. Roosevelt and Elinor Morgenthau had dinner with Lillian Wald and some other women in the summer of 1961. The guest list has been fictionalized, and the conversations reported are all fiction. Jane Addams visited Leo Tolstoy, and he may have criticized her dress and her failure to work with the people. But the recounting of it has been fictionalized. Margaret Sanger's story of troubles related to her work to educate women about birth control is a fictionalized recounting of actual events.

Walter White, W. E. B. Du Bois and the NAACP produced a document, "An Appeal to the World: A Statement of Denial of Human Rights to Minorities in the Case of Citizens of Negro Descent in the United States of America and an Appeal to the United Nations for Redress" which was submitted to the United Nations Human Rights division in 1947. They asked Mrs. Roosevelt to submit the document with them, and she declined. The story of Callie House is a fictionalized version of a true story. I learned of her work with the National Ex-Slave Mutual Relief, Bounty and Pension Association through Mary Frances Berry's book, *My Face is Black is True: Callie House and the Struggle for Ex-Slave Reparations*.

Mrs. Roosevelt traveled to Japan on two occasions. The itineraries, actions and conversations described are fiction. The prayer included in Mrs. Roosevelt's letter regarding her second trip to Japan was cited in her March 6, 1940 "My Day" Column, she mentions it as part of a service at St. John's Church in Washington DC. (Eleanor Roosevelt, "My Day, March 6, 1940," *The Eleanor Roosevelt Papers Digital Edition* (2017), https://www2.gwu.edu/~erpapers/myday/displaydoc.cfm?_y=1940&_f=md055520.) Her son Elliot has written that his mother prayed that prayer every night before she went to sleep.

Mrs. Roosevelt was hospitalized in the fall of 1962, but the description of events at the hospital are fictional.
Because the United Nations *Universal Declaration of Human Rights* is central to many of Mrs. Roosevelt's letters, I've included a copy of that document here. And because I am an academic at heart, following the Declaration of Human Rights I've included a list of a few of the books central in informing my thinking related to Mrs. Roosevelt.

Enjoy!

## *The United Nations Universal Declaration of Human Rights*

(http://www.un.org/en/universal-declaration-human-rights/)

The Universal Declaration of Human Rights (UDHR) is a milestone document in the history of human rights. Drafted by representatives with different legal and cultural backgrounds from all regions of the world, the Declaration was proclaimed by the United Nations General Assembly in Paris on 10 December 1948 (General Assembly resolution 217 A) as a common standard of achievements for all peoples and all nations. It sets out, for the first time, fundamental human rights to be universally protected. It has been translated into over 500 languages.

**Preamble**

Whereas recognition of the inherent dignity and of the equal and inalienable rights of all members of the human family is the foundation of freedom, justice and peace in the world,

Whereas disregard and contempt for human rights have resulted in barbarous acts which have outraged the conscience of mankind, and the advent of a world in which human beings shall enjoy freedom of speech and belief and freedom from fear and want has been proclaimed as the highest aspiration of the common people,

Whereas it is essential, if man is not to be compelled to have recourse, as a last resort, to rebellion against tyranny and oppression, that human rights should be protected by the rule of law,

Whereas it is essential to promote the development of friendly relations between nations,

Whereas the peoples of the United Nations have in the Charter reaffirmed their faith in fundamental human rights, in the dignity and worth of the human person and in the equal rights of men and women and have determined to promote social progress and better standards of life in larger freedom,
Whereas Member States have pledged themselves to achieve, in cooperation with the United Nations, the promotion of universal respect for and observance of human rights and fundamental freedoms,

Whereas a common understanding of these rights and freedoms is of the greatest importance for the full realization of this pledge,

Now, Therefore THE GENERAL ASSEMBLY proclaims THIS UNIVERSAL DECLARATION OF HUMAN RIGHTS as a common standard of achievement for all peoples and all nations, to the end that every individual and every organ of society, keeping this Declaration constantly in mind, shall strive by teaching and education to promote respect for these rights and freedoms and by progressive measures, national and international, to secure their universal and effective recognition and observance, both among the peoples of Member States themselves and among the peoples of territories under their jurisdiction.

**Article 1.**

All human beings are born free and equal in dignity and rights. They are endowed with reason and conscience and should act towards one another in a spirit of brotherhood.

**Article 2.**

Everyone is entitled to all the rights and freedoms set forth in this Declaration, without distinction of any kind, such as race, color, sex, language, religion, political or other opinion, national or social origin, property, birth or other status. Furthermore, no distinction shall be made on the basis of the political, jurisdictional or international status of the country or territory to which a person belongs, whether it be independent, trust, non-self-governing or under any other limitation of sovereignty.

**Article 3.**

Everyone has the right to life, liberty and security of person.

**Article 4.**

No one shall be held in slavery or servitude; slavery and the slave trade shall be prohibited in all their forms.

**Article 5.**

No one shall be subjected to torture or to cruel, inhuman or degrading treatment or punishment.

**Article 6.**

Everyone has the right to recognition everywhere as a person before the law.

**Article 7.**

All are equal before the law and are entitled without any discrimination to equal protection of the law. All are entitled to equal protection against any discrimination in violation of this Declaration and against any incitement to such discrimination.

**Article 8.**

Everyone has the right to an effective remedy by the competent national tribunals for acts violating the fundamental rights granted him by the constitution or by law.

**Article 9.**

No one shall be subjected to arbitrary arrest, detention or exile.

**Article 10.**

Everyone is entitled in full equality to a fair and public hearing by an independent and impartial tribunal, in the determination of his rights and obligations and of any criminal charge against him.

**Article 11.**

(1) Everyone charged with a penal offense has the right to be presumed innocent until proved guilty according to law in a public trial at which he has had all the guarantees necessary for his defense.
(2) No one shall be held guilty of any penal offense on account of any act or omission which did not constitute a penal offense, under national or international law, at the time when it was committed. Nor shall a heavier penalty be imposed than the one that was applicable at the time the penal offense was committed.

**Article 12.**

No one shall be subjected to arbitrary interference with his privacy, family, home or correspondence, nor to attacks upon his honor and reputation. Everyone has the right to the protection of the law against such interference or attacks.

**Article 13.**

(1) Everyone has the right to freedom of movement and residence within the borders of each state.

(2) Everyone has the right to leave any country, including his own, and to return to his country.

**Article 14.**

(1) Everyone has the right to seek and to enjoy in other countries asylum from persecution.

(2) This right may not be invoked in the case of prosecutions genuinely arising from non-political crimes or from acts contrary to the purposes and principles of the United Nations.

**Article 15.**

(1) Everyone has the right to a nationality.

(2) No one shall be arbitrarily deprived of his nationality nor denied the right to change his nationality.

**Article 16.**

(1) Men and women of full age, without any limitation due to race, nationality or religion, have the right to marry and to found a family. They are entitled to equal rights as to marriage, during marriage and at its dissolution.

(2) Marriage shall be entered into only with the free and full consent of the intending spouses.

(3) The family is the natural and fundamental group unit of society and is entitled to protection by society and the State.

**Article 17.**

(1) Everyone has the right to own property alone as well as in association with others.

(2) No one shall be arbitrarily deprived of his property.

**Article 18.**

Everyone has the right to freedom of thought, conscience and religion; this right includes freedom to change his religion or belief, and freedom, either alone or in community with others and in public or private, to manifest his religion or belief in teaching, practice, worship and observance.

**Article 19.**

Everyone has the right to freedom of opinion and expression; this right includes freedom to hold opinions without interference and to seek, receive and impart information and ideas through any media and regardless of frontiers.

**Article 20.**

(1) Everyone has the right to freedom of peaceful assembly and association.

(2) No one may be compelled to belong to an association.

**Article 21.**

(1) Everyone has the right to take part in the government of his country, directly or through freely chosen representatives.

(2) Everyone has the right of equal access to public service in his country.

(3) The will of the people shall be the basis of the authority of government; this will shall be expressed in periodic and genuine elections which shall be by universal and equal suffrage and shall be held by secret vote or by equivalent free voting procedures.

**Article 22.**

Everyone, as a member of society, has the right to social security and is entitled to realization, through national effort and international cooperation and in accordance with the organization and resources of each State, of the economic, social and cultural rights indispensable for his dignity and the free development of his personality.

**Article 23.**

(1) Everyone has the right to work, to free choice of employment, to just and favorable conditions of work and to protection against unemployment.

(2) Everyone, without any discrimination, has the right to equal pay for equal work.

(3) Everyone who works has the right to just and favorable remuneration ensuring for himself and his family an existence worthy of human dignity, and supplemented, if necessary, by other means of social protection.

(4) Everyone has the right to form and to join trade unions for the protection of his interests.

**Article 24.**

Everyone has the right to rest and leisure, including reasonable limitation of working hours and periodic holidays with pay.

**Article 25.**

(1) Everyone has the right to a standard of living adequate for the health and well-being of himself and of his family, including food, clothing, housing and medical care and necessary social services, and the right to security in the event of unemployment, sickness, disability, widowhood, old age or other lack of livelihood in circumstances beyond his control.

(2) Motherhood and childhood are entitled to special care and assistance. All children, whether born in or out of wedlock, shall enjoy the same social protection.

**Article 26.**

(1) Everyone has the right to education. Education shall be free, at least in the elementary and fundamental stages. Elementary education shall be compulsory. Technical and professional education shall be made generally available and higher education shall be equally accessible to all on the basis of merit.

(2) Education shall be directed to the full development of the human personality and to the strengthening of respect for human rights and fundamental freedoms. It shall promote understanding, tolerance and friendship among all nations, racial or religious groups, and shall further the activities of the United Nations for the maintenance of peace.

(3) Parents have a prior right to choose the kind of education that shall be given to their children.

**Article 27.**

(1) Everyone has the right freely to participate in the cultural life of the community, to enjoy the arts and to share in scientific advancement and its benefits.

(2) Everyone has the right to the protection of the moral and material interests resulting from any scientific, literary or artistic production of which he is the author.

**Article 28.**

Everyone is entitled to a social and international order in which the rights and freedoms set forth in this Declaration can be fully realized.

**Article 29.**

(1) Everyone has duties to the community in which alone the free and full development of his personality is possible.

(2) In the exercise of his rights and freedoms, everyone shall be subject only to such limitations as are determined by law solely for the purpose of securing due recognition and respect for the rights and freedoms of others and of meeting the just requirements of morality, public order and the general welfare in a democratic society.

(3) These rights and freedoms may in no case be exercised contrary to the purposes and principles of the United Nations.

**Article 30.**

Nothing in this Declaration may be interpreted as implying for any State, group or person any right to engage in any activity or to perform any act aimed at the destruction of any of the rights and freedoms set forth herein.

## *For Further Reading*

Glendon, Mary Ann. 2002. *A World Made New: Eleanor Roosevelt and the Universal Declaration of Human Rights. (*This is the book that inspired the novel.*)*

Cook, Blanche Wiesen (perhaps the most in depth biography of ER)
1992. *Eleanor Roosevelt, Vol. 1*: 1884-1933.
1999. *Eleanor Roosevelt: Volume 2: The Defining Years*, 1933-1938.
2016. *Eleanor Roosevelt, Volume 3: The War Years and After*, 1939-1962

Lash, Joseph P. (ER's friend and biographer)
1972. *Eleanor: The Years Alone*. New York: W.W. Norton,
1984. *Life was Meant to be Lived: A Centenary Portrait of Eleanor Roosevelt*. New York: W.W. Norton,
1984. *A World of Love: Eleanor Roosevelt and Her Friends, 1943–1962*. Garden City, New York: Doubleday,
*1985. Love, Eleanor: Eleanor Roosevelt and her friends*. McGraw-Hill; 1st McGraw-Hill
Berry, Mary Francis. 2006. *My Face is Black is True: Callie House and the Struggle for Ex-Slave Reparations*. Vintage.

## *Yiddish & Hebrew words used*

Bubba—grandmother.

Chazzer—pig.

Kibbutz—a collective agricultural community in Israel.

Kasefet—Hebrew for safe. The name of a fictional kibbutz in the northwestern Negev Desert in Israel, also used as the name of a fictional crossing between Israel and Gaza.

Mazel tov—congratulations.

Mensch—a person of integrity and honor.

Mitga'aga'at—I am missing you.

Tsoris—trouble or misfortune.

Zayde—grandfather.

# Acknowledgements

No book is written without the generous help and support of an extensive cast of characters.

Thanks to Lisa Gebo and John Michelle who were among the first to believe I could write a book. May their memory be a blessing.

My heartfelt thanks to Dorothy Van Soest, who encouraged me to take up fiction, who then read and reread SO many drafts. Dorothy, your insights are always spot on, thank you for everything. Thanks to Max Regan and Lisa Berman your keen editing helped me to develop the story's potential.

Thanks to my sister, Ruth Ann Balla for thoughtfully reading SO many versions, and for noticing what needed to be included. Thanks to Jean McCloskey for always being my sister. Thanks to Charleen Alderfer, Kelly Ward, Victor Deihl and Stuart Roe, Jan Evans and Donna Smith for reading and discussing early drafts of the manuscript. The feedback sharpened my thinking and expanded my imagination. The book is better for our conversations.

Thanks to Linda and Peter Craig for telling me Sybil Ludington's story; to Rachel Naomi Remen for her telling of the *tikkun olam* story. Thanks to Harriet Cohen, Alayna Berg, Orly Krupkin and Sori Wolk Yudkowsky for insights regarding Jewish community life and Israeli kibbutzim. Special thanks to Stephanie Busby for producing my first 'book' *Utopia*—it was a most delicious cake.

Thanks to Hunter Bishop for saying yes.

More thanks than I can ever articulate go to MaryLou Ramsey, for reading more versions of the manuscript than either of us care to count; for gentle insights, for waiting while I finished one more revision; and for always being there with me and for me.

MaryLou, with you, life has grace and dignity.

Made in the USA
Monee, IL
19 June 2022